Introduction to Statistics

AN INTUITIVE GUIDE FOR ANALYZING DATA AND UNLOCKING DISCOVERIES

Jim Frost

Statistics By Jim Publishing

STATE COLLEGE, PENNSYLVANIA

U.S.A.

Published by: Statistics By Jim Publishing

State College, PA 16801

Visit the author's website: statisticsbyjim.com

To contact the author, please email: jim@statisticsbyjim.com.

Ordering Information: Quantity sales. Special discounts are available on quantity purchases. For details, contact the email address above.

Introduction to Statistics: An Intuitive Guide for Analyzing Data and Unlocking Discoveries / Jim Frost. —1st ed.

ISBN 978-1-7354311-0-9

Contents

INTRODUCTION

Prepare for an Adventure!

I love statistics and analyzing data! I also love talking and writing about it. I was a researcher at a major university. Then, I spent over a decade working at a major statistical software company. During my time at the software company, I learned how to present statistics in a manner that makes it more intuitive. I want you to understand the essential concepts, practices, and knowledge for statistics so you can analyze your data confidently. That's the goal of my book.

Over the years, I've literally received thousands of requests from aspiring data scientists for statistical guidance. This book is my answer - years of knowledge and thousands of hours of hard work distilled into a thorough, practical guide for understanding statistics.

I hope this book helps you see statistics through my eyes–as a key that can unlock discoveries trapped in your data. Discovery is a bumpy road. There might be statistical challenges en route, but they can be exciting and rewarding to resolve. Sometimes it is the perplexing mystery in your data that prompts you to play detective and leads you to surprising discoveries!

I hope you'll view this book as a voyage. We start with the practical nuts and bolts about the field of statistics and data analysis. Then we move to the broader context of the process and challenges of using statistics to expand human knowledge. Now, that's an adventure in statistics!

In this book, you'll learn about the many facets of the field of statistics. We'll start with an overview of statistics and why it is so important. Then, we move on to the necessary skills and knowledge about the different types of data, and how to summarize data both graphically and numerically. Importantly, I'll show you how to discover relationships between your variables. After that, we go to the next level and learn about populations and how to estimate their properties using samples.

Finally, we look at how statistics are part of the scientific method and help expand the scope of human knowledge. This process includes designing experiments that identify causation, rather than mere correlation, by accounting for challenges that all studies face. The book closes with criteria you can use to evaluate the quality of both the data and the design of the experiment itself. These criteria are useful for critiquing your research or other researchers' experiments.

Reading this book will allow you to take your skills to the next level. You'll be able to proceed onto more advanced statistical studies such as hypothesis testing, regression analysis, and experimental design. Alternatively, you'll have a solid foundation for a career in data science and machine learning.

You'll notice that there are not many equations in this book. After all, you should let your statistical software handle the calculations while you instead focus on understanding your results. Consequently, I focus on the concepts and practices that you'll need to know to perform the analysis and interpret the results correctly. I'll use more graphs than equations! If you need the equations, you'll find them in most textbooks.

Please note that throughout this book I use Minitab statistical software. However, this book is not about teaching particular software but rather how to perform basic graphing and analysis. All common statistical software packages should be able to perform the analyses that I show. There is nothing in here that is unique to Minitab.

Throughout this book, I use datasets that you can download from my website so you can learn by doing. To download them, go to:

https://statisticsbyjim.com/introductionstatistics

CHAPTER 1

The Importance of Statistics

Statistics are everywhere today. You'll run across them in your everyday life. Four of five dentists prefer this toothpaste! On the news. This scientific poll used random sampling and has a margin of error of 3%. In school. Your grades were averages of scores. Perhaps you were graded on a curve? Then, you took the SAT, ACT, or GRE and received your results with percentiles. You'll find statistics in almost every aspect of life: Nielsen TV ratings, surveys, political polls, insurance rates, and so on. And then, of course, there are the ubiquitous sports statistics, batting averages, third-down conversions, and countless more! Politicians and policy wonks use statistics to make their cases. Companies use statistics to use data to make decisions and increase their profits.

The field of statistics is crucial for expanding scientific knowledge. Statistical analyses are present in virtually every scientific study. Indeed, these analyses determine whether the results of the study are significant and worthy of being published. It's powerful stuff. But what is the field of statistics exactly?

The field of statistics is the science of learning from data. Statistical knowledge helps you use the proper methods to collect the data, employ the correct analyses, and effectively present the results. Statistics is a crucial process behind how we make discoveries in science, make decisions based on data, and make predictions. Statistics allows you to understand a subject much more deeply. Surprisingly, the field isn't only about numeric results. It also involves a wide range of practices, decisions, and methodologies for both collecting data and analyzing them in a manner that produces valid findings and sound conclusions.

Let's start by covering two main reasons why studying the field of statistics is crucial in modern society. First, statisticians are guides for learning from data and navigating common problems that can lead you to incorrect conclusions. Second, given the growing importance of decisions and opinions based on data, it's crucial that you can critically assess the quality of analyses that others present to you.

In my view, statistics is an exciting field about the thrill of discovery, learning, and challenging your assumptions. Statistics facilitates the creation of new knowledge. Bit by bit, we push back the frontier of what is known.

Draw Valid Conclusions

Statistics are not just numbers and facts. You know, things like 4 out of 5 dentists prefer a specific toothpaste. Instead, it's an array of knowledge and procedures that allow you to learn from data reliably. Statistics enable you to evaluate claims based on quantitative evidence and help you differentiate between reasonable and dubious conclusions. That aspect is particularly vital these days because data are so plentiful along with interpretations presented by people with an agenda.

Statisticians offer critical guidance in producing trustworthy analyses and predictions. Along the way, statisticians can help investigators avoid a wide variety of analytical traps.

When analysts use statistical procedures correctly, they tend to produce accurate results. In fact, statistical analyses account for uncertainty and error in the results. Statisticians ensure that all aspects of a study follow the appropriate methods to produce reliable results.

These methods include:

- Collecting reliable data.
- Analyzing the data appropriately.
- Drawing reasonable conclusions.

Avoid Common Pitfalls

Please notice that statistical practices begin *before* the analysis phase! Using statistical analyses to produce findings for a study is the culmination of a long process. This process includes constructing the study design, selecting and measuring the variables, devising the sampling technique and sample size, cleaning the data, and determining the analysis methodology among numerous other issues. The overall quality of the results depends on the entire chain of events. A single weak link might produce unreliable results. The following list provides a small taste of potential problems and analytical errors that can affect a study.

Biased samples: An incorrectly drawn sample can bias the conclusions from the start. For example, if a study uses human subjects, the subjects might be different than non-subjects in a way that affects the results.

Overgeneralization: Findings from one population might not apply to another population. Statistical inferences are always limited, and you must understand the limitations.

Causality: How do you determine when X causes a change in Y? Statisticians need tight standards to assume causality, whereas others accept causal relationships more easily. When A precedes B, and A correlates with B, many mistakenly believe it is a causal connection! However, you'll need to use an experimental design that includes random assignment to assume confidently that the results represent causality.

Incorrect analysis: Are you analyzing a multivariate study area with only one variable? Or, using an inadequate set of variables? Perhaps you're assessing the mean when the median might be better? You can use a wide range of analytical tools, but not all of them are correct for a specific situation.

Violating the assumptions for an analysis: Most statistical analyses have assumptions. These assumptions often involve properties of the sample, variables, data, and the model. Adding to the complexity, you can waive some assumptions under specific conditions—sometimes thanks to the central limit theorem. When you violate an essential assumption, you risk producing misleading results.

Data mining: Even when analysts do everything else correctly, they can produce falsely significant results by investigating a dataset for too long. When analysts conduct many tests, some will be statistically significant due to chance patterns in the data. Fastidious statisticians track the number of tests performed during a study and place the results in the proper context.

Numerous considerations must be correct to produce trustworthy conclusions. Unfortunately, there are many ways to mess up analyses and produce misleading results. Statisticians can guide others through this swamp! We'll cover everything, and more, on that list.

Make an Impact in Your Field

Researchers use statistical analyses in almost all fields to make sense of the vast amount of available data. Even if the field of statistics is not your primary field of study, it can help you make an impact in your

Statistics	**Anecdotal Evidence**
Samples are large and representative. Using proper methodologies, they are generalizable outside the sample.	Small, biased samples are not generalizable.
Scientists take precise measurements in controlled environments with calibrated equipment.	Unplanned observations are described orally or in writing.
Other relevant factors are measured and controlled.	Pertinent factors are ignored.
Strict requirements for identifying causal connections.	Anecdotes assume causal relationships as a matter of fact.

A quick look at the table should be enough to convince you that anecdotal evidence is not trustworthy! However, it's even worse thanks to psychological factors that prime us for believing these stories.

Humans are more likely to tell and remember dramatic, extraordinary personal stories. Throw in some emotion, and you're more likely to believe the story. In psychological terms, statistical analysis of data that scientists collect carefully from well-designed experiments lacks that emotional kick. Sad but true.

Furthermore, if B follows A, our brains are wired to assume that A causes B.

Finally, anecdotal evidence cherry-picks the best stories. You don't hear about all of the unsuccessful cases because people are less likely to talk about them.

When Fred tells an emotional story about taking a supplement and losing a lot of weight, we'll remember it and assume the supplement caused the weight loss. Unfortunately, we don't hear from the other ten people who took the supplement and didn't lose weight. We also don't know what else Fred might be doing to lose weight.

Collectively, these factors bias conclusions drawn from anecdotal evidence towards abnormal outcomes and unjustified causal connections.

Next, I'll illustrate the problems graphically and explain how statistics and the scientific method deal with them.

The graph below displays the results from anecdotal stories of people who took a hypothetical weight loss supplement. Think of this chart as a summary of the results presented in a TV commercial. We'll even assume these people are telling the complete truth. The supplement looks effective, right? They've lost a lot of weight! When you see the individuals and hear their emotional stories about weight loss, we want to believe that the supplement worked.

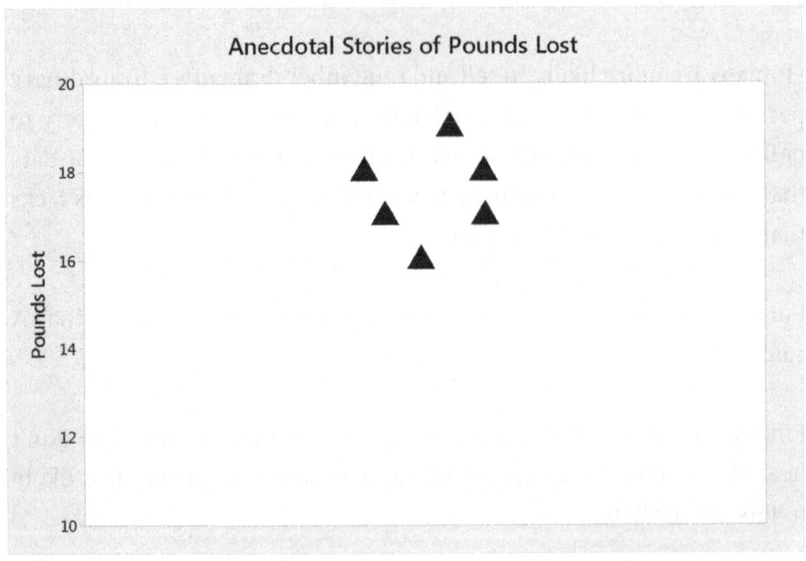

Regrettably, the graph doesn't provide the full story. Remember, anecdotal evidence uses small non-random samples that aren't generalizable beyond the sample. The individuals might have been cherry-picked for their narratives, or perhaps they presented the tales on their own. Either way, it is a sample based on having a dramatic and emotionally compelling story. As the fine print says, their results are not typical!

Unfortunately, our minds are wired to believe this type of evidence. We place more weight on dramatic, personal stories.

A scientific study of the weight loss supplement

Now, imagine we conduct a scientific experiment using a more substantial, random sample that represents the broader population. We'll also include a treatment and control group for comparison. We must go beyond a few compelling stories and get the bigger picture that scientific studies can provide.

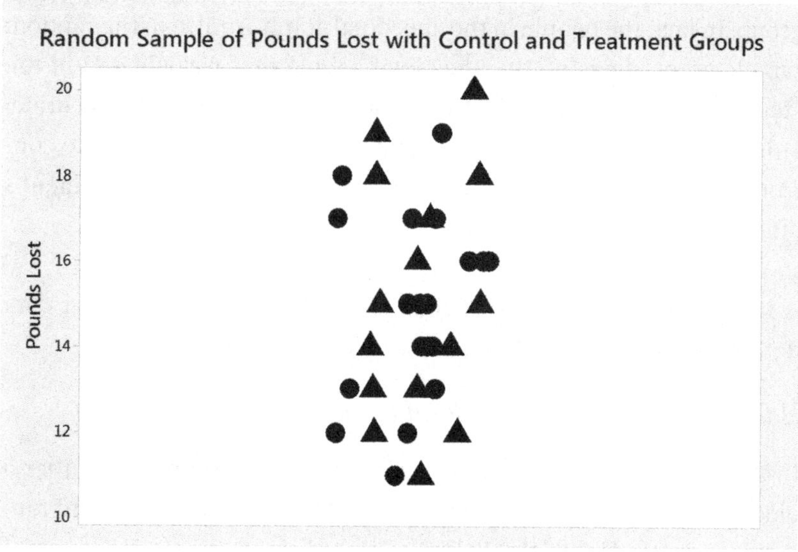

In this graph, triangles again represent supplement takers, and circles represent those who didn't take the supplement. These results are not as impressive as the anecdotal graph. Why? Together, random sampling and the control group create an unbiased picture with a broader context.

Notice how some who took the supplement lost the weight shown in the TV ad, but many more lost much less weight. Those people didn't come forward with their less exciting stories! Furthermore, participants in the control group did not take the supplement, but they fit the same weight loss pattern as those who did. Collectively, taking the supplement didn't produce more substantial weight loss than the control group.

Because our supplement study uses a random sample that represents the population, rather than a self-selected sample, we have reason to believe we can apply these results outside the sample.

Anecdotal stories are not necessarily fictional. Instead, they don't represent typical results, account for other factors, and have no control group. In fact, the people in the anecdotal graph are also in the random sample graph. Imagine the anecdotal people first participated in the study and then appeared in the TV ad. Their accounts are accurate. However, after they self-select to appear in the ad and there is no control group, their stories provide a false impression of the supplement's effectiveness.

A key lesson throughout this book is that how you collect your data determines what, if anything, you can learn from them.

How Statistics Beats Anecdotal Evidence

In statistics, there are two basic methods for determining whether a dietary supplement causes weight loss: observational studies and randomized controlled trials (RCTs).

In an observational study, scientists measure all pertinent variables in a representative sample and then generate a statistical model that describes the role of each variable. For each subject, you measure variables such as basal metabolic rate, exercise, diet, health, etc., and the consumption of dietary supplements. After you factor in the role of all other relevant variables, you can determine whether the supplement correlates with weight loss. Anecdotal evidence provides none of this critical, contextual information.

Randomized controlled trials (RCTs) is the other method. RCTs are the gold standard because they allow you to draw causal conclusions about the treatment effect. After all, we want to determine whether the supplement causes weight loss. RCTs assign subjects to treatment and control groups randomly. This process helps ensure that the groups are comparable when treatment begins. Consequently, treatment effects are the most likely cause for differences between groups at the end of the study.

Don't worry. We'll cover all of this information about experiments in much greater detail starting in chapter 7. For now, understand that using data to identify causal relationships (the supplement causes the weight loss) and being able to generalize the results beyond the original sample requires the researchers to use various data collecting procedures and experimental designs.

Making decisions based on anecdotal evidence might not always be harmful. For example, if you ask a friend for a restaurant recommendation, the risk is low, especially if you know his/her tastes. However, if you're making important decisions about things like finances, healthcare, and fitness, don't base them on anecdotal evidence. Look at scientific data and expert analysis even though they're not as flashy as emotionally charged stories presented by relatable people!

If you find yourself being won over by anecdotal evidence, remind yourself that the results are not typical!

Organization of this Book

Unless you are involved with data analysis, you're probably more familiar with the graphical and numeric results that someone else produced. However, the field of statistics covers much more than that, including a wide variety of processes and methodologies for producing trustworthy results.

Consequently, I've split this book into two major parts.

The first portion covers the essential tools of the trade, including data types, summarizing the data, and identifying relationships between variables. I'll describe the types of data and how to present them graphically. Learn how summary statistics represent an entire dataset and describe where an observation falls within it. These statistics include measures of central tendency, measures of variability, percentiles, and correlation. Then, we'll move onto probability distributions. Probability distributions help you understand the distribution of values and calculate probabilities. We'll pay extra attention to the crucial Normal Distribution.

Collectively, this knowledge allows you to understand the basics of the different types of data, how to summarize a dataset, identify relationships between different types of variables, and use probabilities to know how the values are distributed. These skills will allow you to summarize a dataset and explain relationships between variables to others.

The second portion covers the practices and procedures for inferential statistics and using statistics in the scientific process. Inferential statistics allow you to use a relatively small sample to learn about an entire population. However, making this leap from a sample to the population requires additional procedures and methodologies. I'll also cover how the field of statistics fits in with the scientific method along with the essentials of designing experiments to answer questions.

CHAPTER 2

Data Types, Graphs, and Finding Relationships

In the field of statistics, data are vital. Data are the information that you collect to learn, draw conclusions, and test hypotheses. After all, statistics is the science of learning from data. However, there are different types of variables, and they record various kinds of information. Crucially, the type of information determines what you can learn from it, and, importantly, what you cannot learn from it. Consequently, you must understand the different types of data.

The term "data" carries strong preconceived notions with it. It almost becomes something separate from reality. Throughout this book, I want you to think about data as information that you are gathering for an inquiry. Data are evidence you can use to answer questions. For example:

- Do flu shots prevent the flu?
- Does exercise improve your health?
- Does a gasoline additive improve gas mileage?

When you assess any of these questions, there's a wide array of characteristics that you can record. For example, in a study that uses human subjects, you can log numerical measurements such as height and weight. However, you can also assign categories, such as gender, marital status, and health issues. You can record counts, such as the number of children. Or, use binary data to record whether a person has the flu or not.

For some characteristics, you can record them in multiple ways. For instance, you can measure a subject's body fat percentage, or you can indicate whether they are medically obese or not.

In this chapter, you'll learn about the different types of variables, what you can learn from them, and how to graph the values using intuitive examples. We'll start with individual variables. Then, I'll show how to use graphs to look for relationships between pairs of different types of variables. For now, we'll only use graphs to gain insights about our data. In chapter 3, we'll start calculating numeric summary statistics.

A relationship between a pair of variables indicates the value of one variable depends on the value of another variable. In other words, if you know the value of one variable, you can predict the value of the other variable more accurately.

Different fields and analysts use several taxonomies for classifying data. For each type of data, I'll provide several synonyms to cover the various classification schemes. Additionally, I'll include small snippets of the data sheet so you can see how the data can appear in your software.

Quantitative versus Qualitative Data

The distinction between quantitative and qualitative data is the most fundamental way to divide types of data. Is the characteristic something you can objectively measure with numbers or not?

Quantitative: The information is recorded as numbers and represents an objective measurement or a count. Temperature, weight, and a count of transactions are all quantitative data. Analysts also refer to this type as numerical data.

Qualitative: The information represents characteristics that you do not measure with numbers. Instead, observations fall within a countable number of groups. This type of variable can capture information that isn't easily measured and can be subjective. Taste, eye color, architectural style, and marital status are all types of qualitative variables.

Within these two broad divisions, there are various subtypes.

Continuous and Discrete Data

When you can represent the information you're gathering with numbers, you are collecting quantitative data. This class encompasses two categories.

Continuous data

Continuous variables can take on any numeric value, and the scale can be meaningfully divided into smaller increments, including fractional and decimal values. There are an infinite number of possible values between any two values. And differences between any two values are always meaningful. Typically, you measure continuous variables on a scale. For example, when you measure height, weight, and temperature, you have continuous data.

Statisticians divide continuous data into two types that you measure using the following scales:

Interval scales: On interval scales, the *interval*, or distance, between any two points is meaningful. For example, the 20-degree difference between 10 and 30 Celsius is equivalent to the difference between 50 and 70 degrees. However, these scales don't have a zero measurement that indicates the lack of the characteristic. For example, Celsius has a zero measure, but it does not mean there is no temperature.

Due to this lack of a true zero, measurement ratios are not valid on interval scales. Thirty degrees Celsius is not three times the temperature as 10 degrees Celsius. You can add and subtract values on an interval scale, but you cannot multiply or divide them.

Ratio scales: On ratio scales, intervals are still meaningful. Additionally, these scales have a zero measurement that represents a lack of the property. For example, zero kilograms indicates a lack of weight. Consequently, measurements *ratios* are valid for these scales. 30 kg is three times the weight of 10 kg. You can add, subtract, multiply, and divide values on a ratio scale.

With continuous variables, you can assess properties such as the mean, median, distribution, range, and standard deviation. For example, the mean height in the U.S. is 5 feet 9 inches for men and 5 feet 4 inches for women. The next chapter covers these summary statistics.

Histograms: Distributions

%Fat
23.9
28.8
32.4
25.8
22.5

Histograms are an excellent way to graph continuous variables because they show the distribution of values. Understanding the distribution allows you to determine which values are more and less common amongst other properties.

Each histogram bar spans a range of values for the continuous variable on the horizontal X-axis. These ranges are also known as bins. The height of each bar represents either the number or proportion of observations that fall within each bin.

The histogram below allows you to assess the distribution of body fat percentage values for adolescent girls. These properties include determining whether the distribution is symmetric or skewed, understanding the spread of values, and identifying where the most common values fall. I'll cover histograms in more detail later in this chapter.

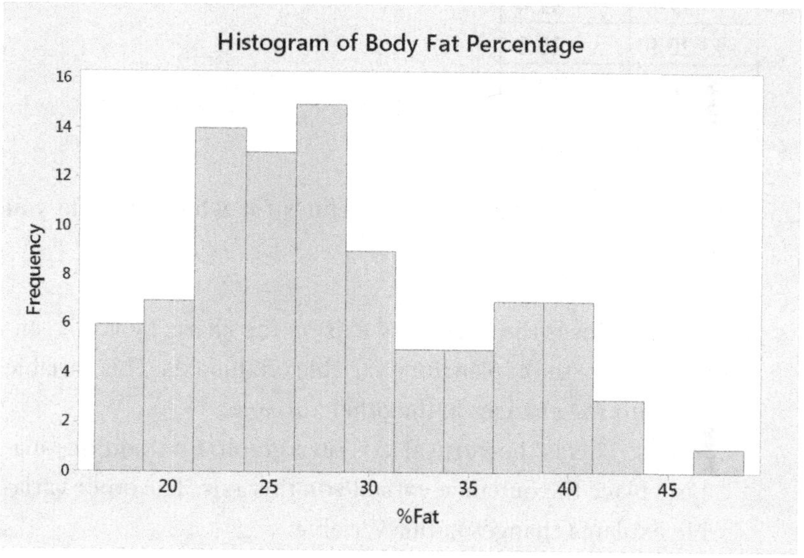

This histogram shows that body fat percentages for most pre-adolescent girls fall between 23-27%. There are no values observed below around 16%. It is also a right-skewed distribution with the right-hand tail of values extending all the way up to 47%.

Please notice that continuous variables allow you to assess the wide variety of properties that I illustrated previously. These include the central tendency, spread, shape of the distribution, and outliers. You'll see a contrast when we get to qualitative variables.

Scatterplots: Trends

When you have two continuous variables, you can graph them using a scatterplot. Scatterplots are great for displaying the relationship between two continuous variables. Each dot on the graph has an X and Y coordinate that corresponds to a pair of values. Each row in the data table contains measurements for one subject or item.

BMI (X)	%Fat (Y)
19.3	23.9
23.0	28.8
27.8	32.4
20.9	25.8
20.4	22.5
20.4	22.1

On scatterplots, statisticians have guidelines for which variable you place along each axis.

- X-axis: This is the horizontal axis on the chart. Typically, analysts place the explanatory variable on this axis. This variable explains the changes in the other variable.
- Y-axis: This is the vertical axis on a graph. By tradition, analysts place the outcome variable on this axis. The other variable explains changes in this variable.

In cases where there isn't a clear explanatory and outcome relationship between variables, it does not matter where you place each variable.

In the scatterplot, each dot represents the body mass index (BMI) and body fat percentage for one research subject in an experiment that I administered.

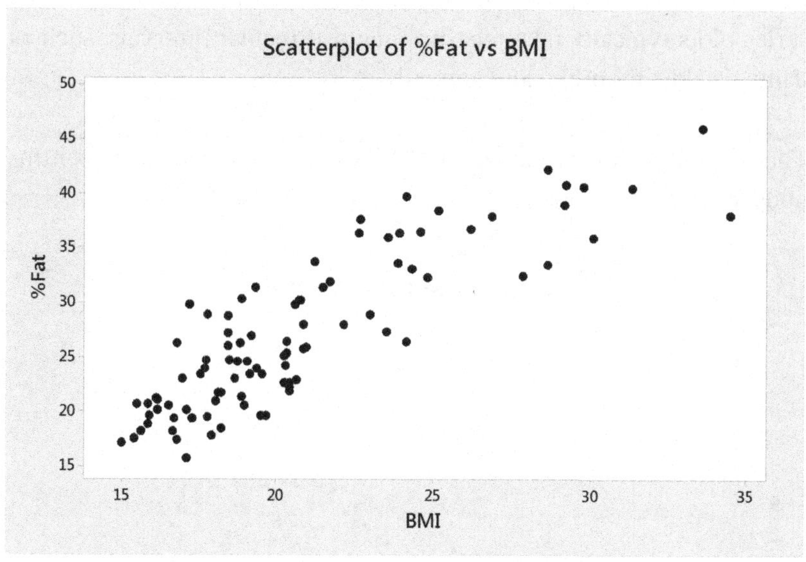

The scatterplot shows how body fat percentage tends to rise as BMI increases. Use correlation to describe the strength of this relationship numerically. We'll cover correlation in chapter 3.

Time Series Plots

Trade
322
317
319
323
327
328

Scatterplots display relationships between pairs of continuous variables. Time series plots do the same, except one of the continuous variables is time. These plots display the continuous variable over time and allow you to determine whether the continuous variable changes over time. You can look for both trends and patterns over time. Time series plots typically take measurements at regular intervals, such as daily, weekly, monthly, and annually.

These graphs display time on the X-axis. The Y-axis shows the continuous measurement scale.

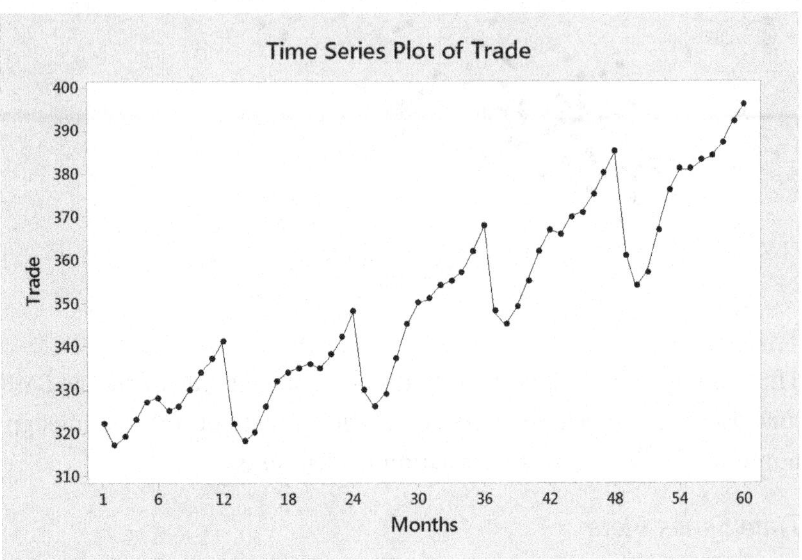

This time series plot displays an upward trend in trade. A cyclical pattern is also apparent.

Discrete data

Car Count
2
1
2
2
3

Discrete quantitative data are a count of the presence of a characteristic, result, item, or activity. These counts are nonnegative integers that cannot be divided into smaller increments. For example, a single household can have 1 or 2 cars, but it cannot have 1.6. There are a finite number of possible values between any two values. Other examples of discrete variables include class sizes, number of candies in a jar, and the number of calls that a call center receives.

With discrete variables, you can calculate and assess a rate of occurrence or a summary of the count, such as the mean, sum, and standard deviation. For example, U.S. households had an average of 2.11 vehicles in 2014.

Bar Charts

Bar charts are a standard way to graph discrete variables. Each bar represents a distinct value, and the height represents its proportion in the entire sample. Use bar charts to indicate which values occur are more and less frequently.

Bar charts and histograms look similar. However, the bars on a histogram touch while they are separate on a bar chart. Each bar on histogram represents a range of values that continuous measurements fall within. On a bar chart, a bar represents one of the discrete values.

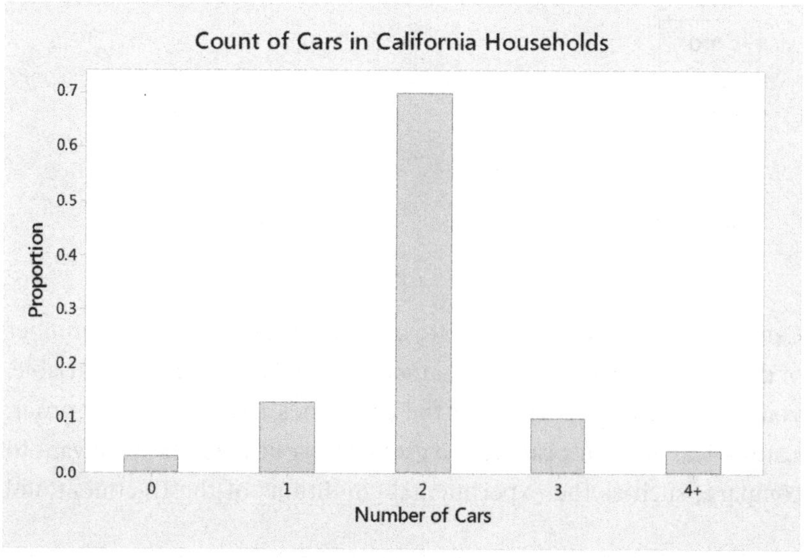

This bar chart indicates that California households with two cars comprise nearly 70% of the sample and are, by far, the most common.

Qualitative Data: Categorical, Binary, and Ordinal

When you record information that categorizes your observations, you are collecting qualitative data. There are three types of qualitative variables—categorical, binary, and ordinal. With these data types, you're often interested in the proportions of each category. Consequently, bar charts and pie charts are conventional methods for graphing qualitative variables because they are useful for displaying counts and relative percentages of each group.

As I mentioned in the section about continuous variables, notice how we learn much less from qualitative data. I highlight this aspect in a later section about binary variables. In cases where you have a choice about recording a characteristic as a continuous or qualitative variable, the best practice is to record the continuous data because you can learn so much more.

Categorical data

Color
White
Silver
Black
Gray
Red

Categorical data have values that you can put into a countable number of distinct groups based on a characteristic. For a categorical variable, you can assign categories, but the categories have no natural order. Categorical variables can define groups in your data that you want to compare, such as the experimental conditions of the treatment and control groups. Analysts also refer to categorical data as both attribute variables and nominal variables.

For example, college major is a categorical variable that can have values such as psychology, political science, engineering, biology, etc.

The categorical data in the pie chart are the results of a PPG Industries study of new car colors in 2012.

Pie charts are great for highlighting the proportions that groups comprise of the whole. You can use them with categorical, binary, and ordinal data that define groups in your sample.

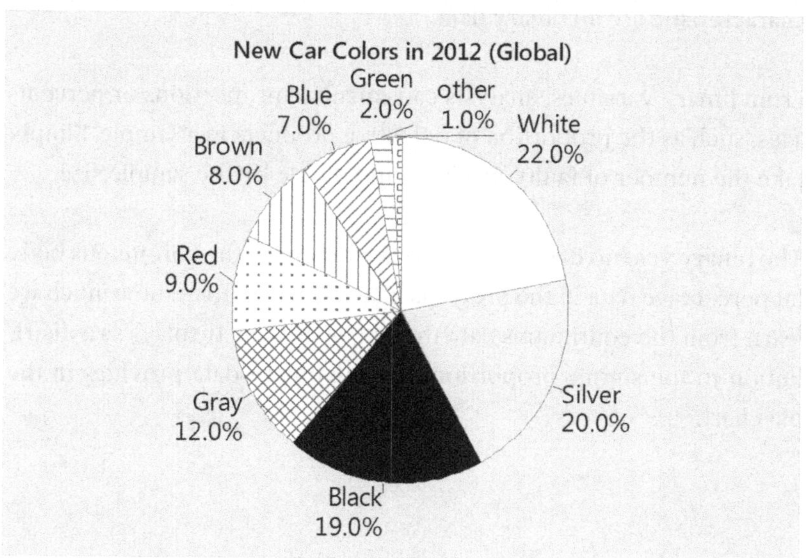

This chart indicates that black, silver, and white cars comprise nearly two-thirds of new cars in the sample. Six other colors cover the remaining third.

Binary data

Obese
Yes
No
No
Yes
No

Binary data can have only two values. If you can place an observation into only two categories, you have a binary variable. Statisticians also refer to binary data as both dichotomous data and indicator variables. For example, pass/fail, male/female, and the presence/absence of a characteristic are all binary data.

From binary variables, analysts can calculate proportions or percentages, such as the proportion of defective products in a sample. Simply take the number of faulty products and divide by the sample size.

The binary yes/no data for the pie chart recodes the continuous body fat percentage data in the previous histogram. Compare how much we learn from the continuous data that the histogram displays as a distribution to the simple proportion that the binary data provides in the pie chart.

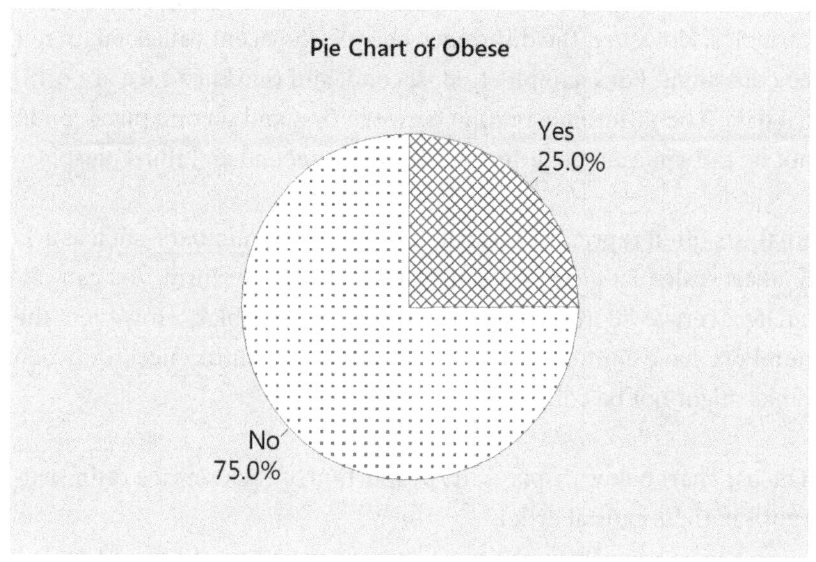

The pie chart indicates that 75% of the sample are not obese, while 25% of the sample are obese.

Ordinal data

Rating
Very Poor
Poor
Neutral
Good
Very Good

Ordinal data have at least three categories, and the categories have a natural order. Examples of ordinal variables include overall status (poor to excellent), agreement (strongly disagree to strongly agree), and rank (such as sporting teams).

Ordinal variables have a combination of qualitative and quantitative properties. On the one hand, these variables have a limited number of discrete values like categorical variables. On the other hand, the differences between values provide some information like quantitative variables. However, the difference between adjacent values might not be consistent. For example, first, second, and third in a race are ordinal data. The difference in time between first and second place might not be the same as the difference between second and third place.

Analysts often represent ordinal variables using numbers, such as a 1-5 Likert scale that measures satisfaction. In number form, you can calculate average scores as with quantitative variables. However, the numbers have limited usefulness because the differences between ranks might not be constant.

The bar chart below displays the proportion of each service rating category in their natural order.

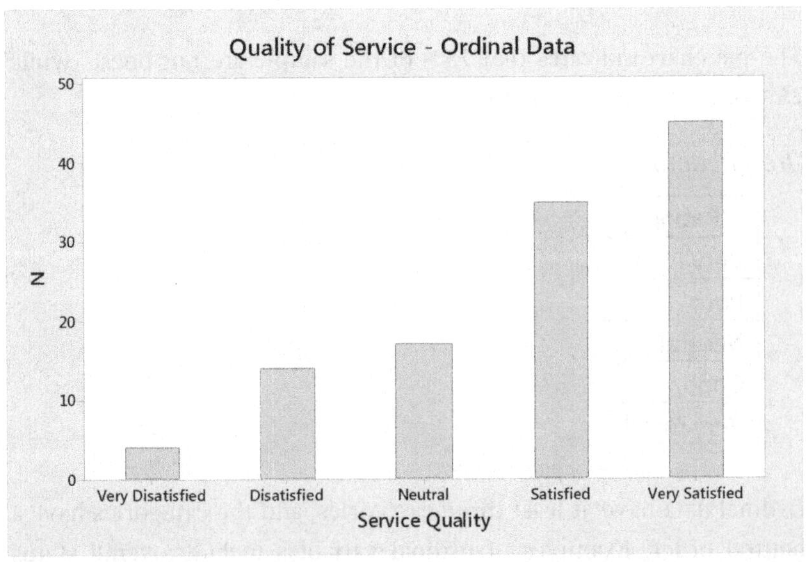

Next Steps

From that overview, you should understand the different types of data, what you can learn from them, and how to graph them.

Previously, I showed how scatterplots display relationships between pairs of continuous variables. In chapter 3, we'll revisit relationships between continuous variables in more detail when we get to correlation.

Up next, let's revisit histograms and see what you can learn from them in more detail. Additionally, I'll show you how to find relationships between a categorical variable and a continuous variable, and pairs of categorical variables.

Histograms in More Detail

Use histograms when you have continuous measurements and want to understand the distribution of values and look for outliers. They are fantastic exploratory tools because they reveal properties about your sample data in ways that summary statistics cannot.

In the field of statistics, we often use summary statistics to describe an entire dataset. These statistics use a single number to quantify a characteristic of the sample. For example, a measure of central tendency is a single value that represents the center point or typical value of a dataset, such as the mean. A measure of variability is another type of summary statistic that describes how spread out the values are in your dataset. The standard deviation is a conventional measure of dispersion. Chapter 3 covers these statistics.

Because I'm a statistician, you probably think I prefer these numeric summaries, but I always recommend that you graph your data before assessing the numbers. The problem with summary statistics is that they are simplifications of your dataset. Graphing the data brings it to life much more fully and intuitively. Generally, I find that using graphs in conjunction with statistics provides the best of both worlds!

In this section, I'll show you how histograms reveal the shape of the distribution, its central tendency, and the spread of values in your sample data. You'll also learn how to identify outliers, how histograms relate to probability distribution functions, and why you might need to use hypothesis tests with them.

I'll also show you how to use histograms to contrast different groups. Comparing properties across groups is a fundamental statistical method that can help you learn about a subject area. As you'll read later in the book, the primary way scientific experiments create new knowledge is by carefully setting up contrasts between groups, such as a treatment and control group.

Amongst other learning objectives, the next several sections illustrate how you can use histograms, boxplots, and individual value plots to compare groups in your data. These types of plots graphically illustrate relationships between a categorical grouping variable and a continuous variable.

Obtain the CSV data file from my website to create most of the histograms in this section. Use the histograms.csv file.

Central Tendency

Use histograms to understand the center of the data. In the histogram, you can see that the center is near 50. Most values in the dataset will be close to 50, and values further away are rarer. The distribution is roughly symmetric, and the values fall between approximately 40 and 64.

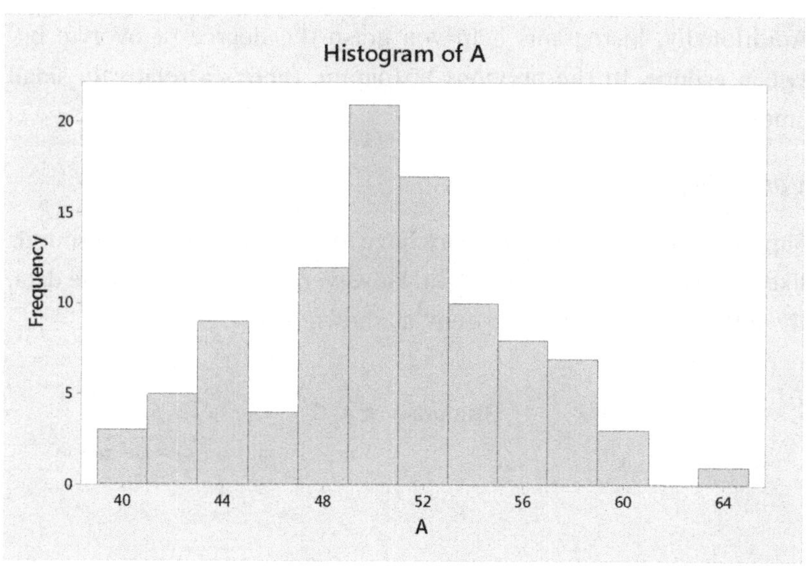

A difference in means shifts the distributions horizontally along the X-axis. In the histogram below, one group has a mean of 50 while the other has a mean of 65.

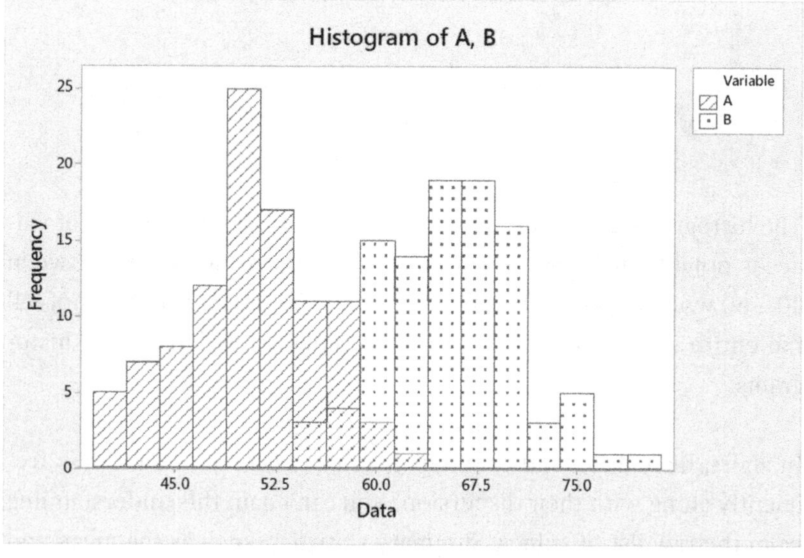

Additionally, histograms help you grasp the degree of overlap between groups. In the previous histogram, there's a relatively small amount of overlap.

Variability

Suppose you hear that two groups have the same mean of 50. It sounds like they're practically equivalent. However, after you graph the data, the differences become apparent, as shown below.

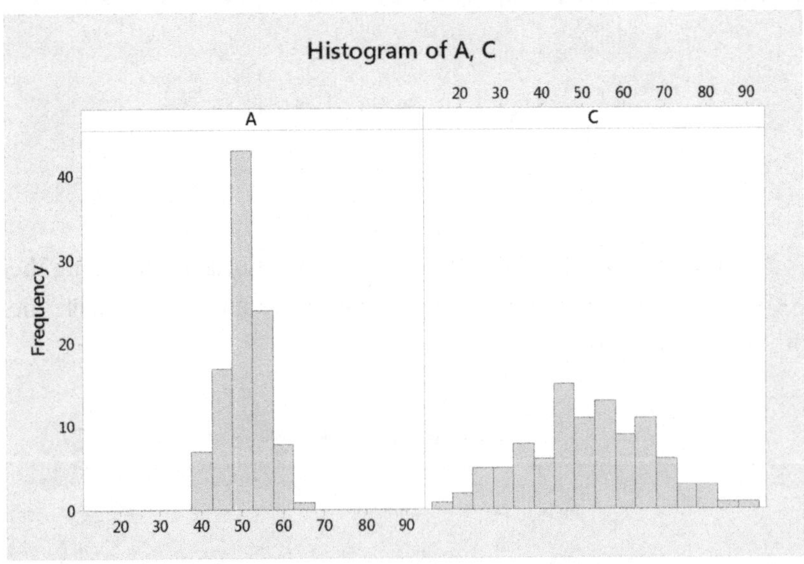

The histograms center on the same value of 50, but the spread of values is notably different. The values for group A mostly fall between 40 – 60 while for group B that range is 20 – 90. The mean does not tell the entire story! At a glance, the difference is evident in the histograms.

In short, histograms indicate which values occur more and less frequently along with their dispersion. You can't gain this understanding from the raw list of values. Summary statistics, such as the mean and standard deviation, will get you partway there. But histograms make the data pop!

Skewed Distributions

Histograms are an excellent tool for identifying the shape of your distribution. So far, we've been looking at symmetric distributions primarily. However, not all distributions are symmetrical. You might have asymmetrical data, also known as a skewed distribution.

The shape of the distribution is a fundamental characteristic of your sample that can determine which measure of central tendency best reflects the center of your data. In this manner, histograms are informative about the summary statistics that are appropriate for your data.

For skewed distributions, the direction the longer tail points defines the direction of skew. The direction of skew indicates where you'll find more values that are further away from the most common values of the distribution.

For right-skewed distributions, the long tail extends to the right while most values cluster on the left, as shown below. These are real data from a study I conducted.

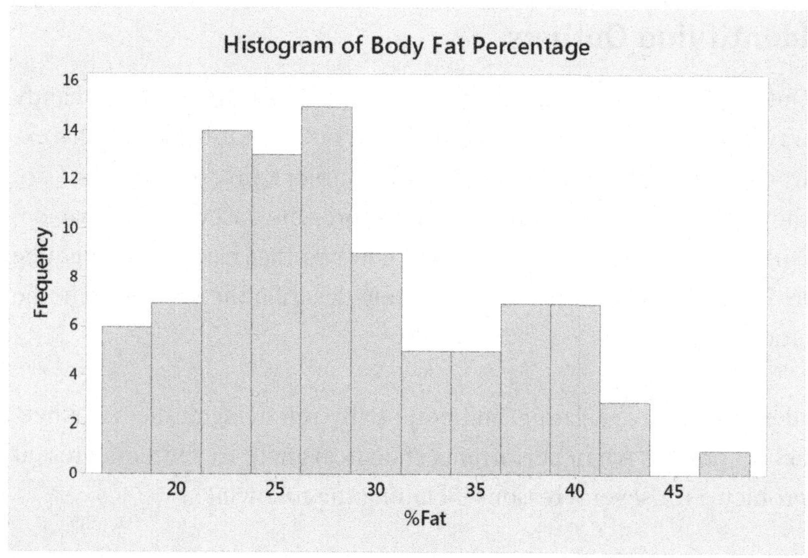

Conversely, for left-skewed distributions, the long tail extends to the left while most values cluster on the right.

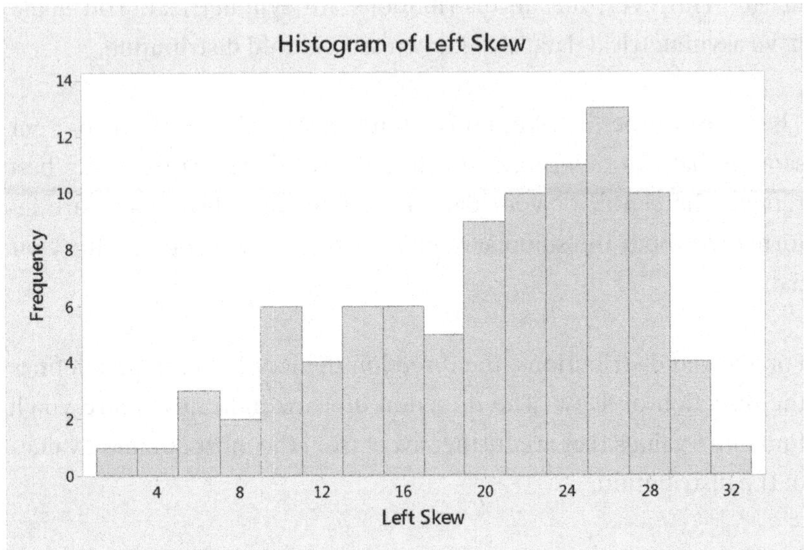

Remember, the direction that the longer tail points defines the type of skew!

Identifying Outliers

Outliers are unusual values in your dataset. Histograms are a handy way to identify outliers. In an instant, you'll see if there are any extreme values. If you identify potential outliers, investigate them. Are they data entry errors, or do they represent observations that occurred under abnormal conditions? On the other hand, they might be legitimate observations that accurately describe the variability in the study area.

Identifying, investigating, and potentially removing outliers is a necessary process when performing statistical analyses. Outliers present problems for several reasons including the following:

- Outliers might not represent the population or research question that you are studying.
- Their extreme values can significantly bias the results of your analyses.
- They might be data entry errors.

However, it's also not always appropriate to remove outliers. You need a sound rationale for doing so.

I cover this process in much greater detail in my ebooks about regression analysis and hypothesis tests.

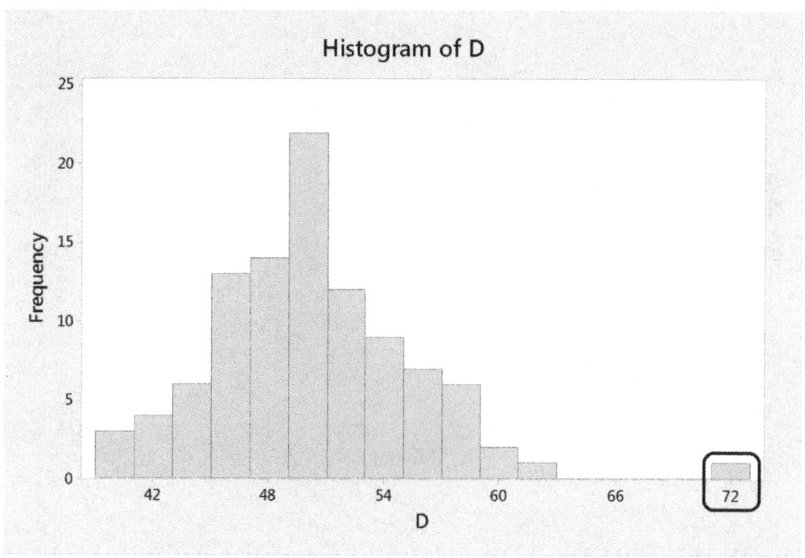

On a histogram, outliers appear as an isolated bar.

Multimodal Distributions

A multimodal distribution has more than one peak. It's easy to miss multimodal distributions when you focus on summary statistics, such as the mean and standard deviations. Consequently, histograms are the best method for detecting multimodal distributions.

Imagine your dataset has the properties shown below.

Descriptive Statistics: Multimodal

Variable	Mean	StDev	Median
Multimodal	59.735	11.513	60.602

That looks relatively straightforward, but when you graph it, you see the following histogram.

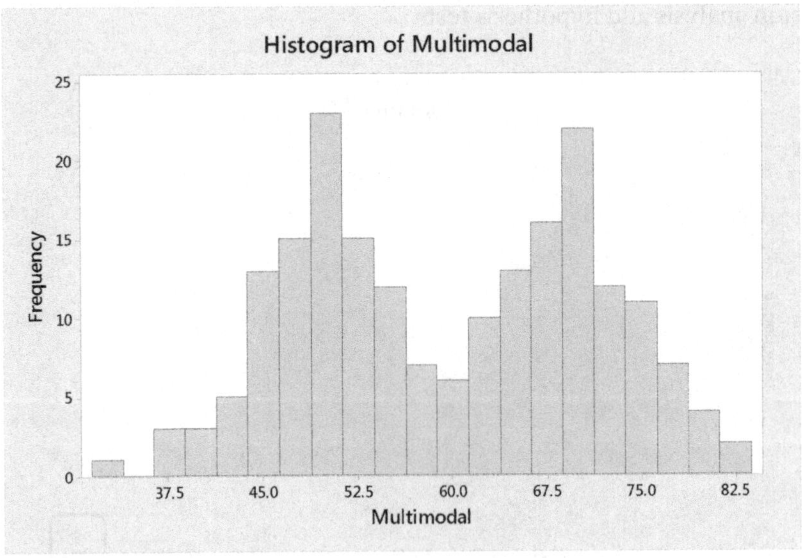

I bet that bimodal distribution was not quite what you were expecting! This histogram illustrates why you should always graph your data rather than just calculating summary statistics!

Identifying Subpopulations

Sometimes these multimodal distributions reflect the actual distribution of the phenomenon that you're studying. In other words, there are genuinely different peak values in the distribution of one population. However, in other cases, multimodal distributions indicate you're combining subpopulations with different characteristics.

Histograms can help confirm the presence of these subpopulations and illustrate how they're different from each other.

Suppose we're studying the heights of American citizens. They have a mean height of 168 centimeters with a standard deviation of 9.8 CM. The histogram is below. There appears to be an unusually broad peak in the center—it's not quite bimodal.

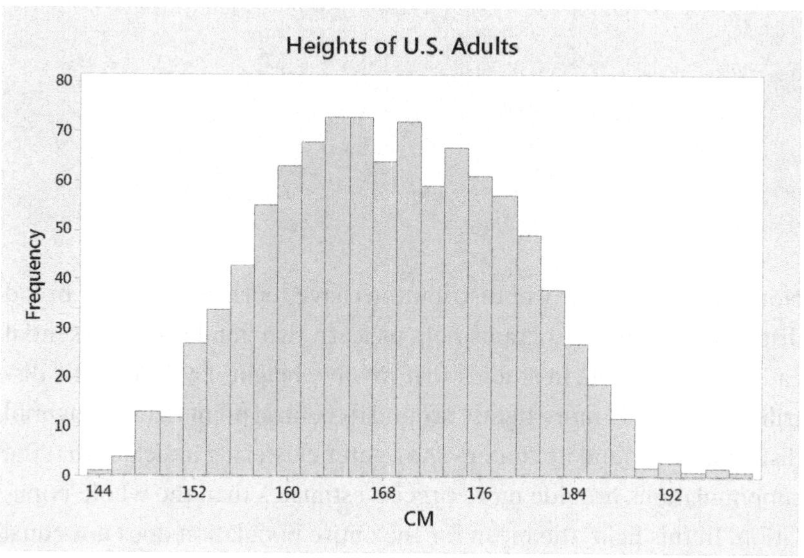

When we divide the sample by gender, the reason for it becomes clear.

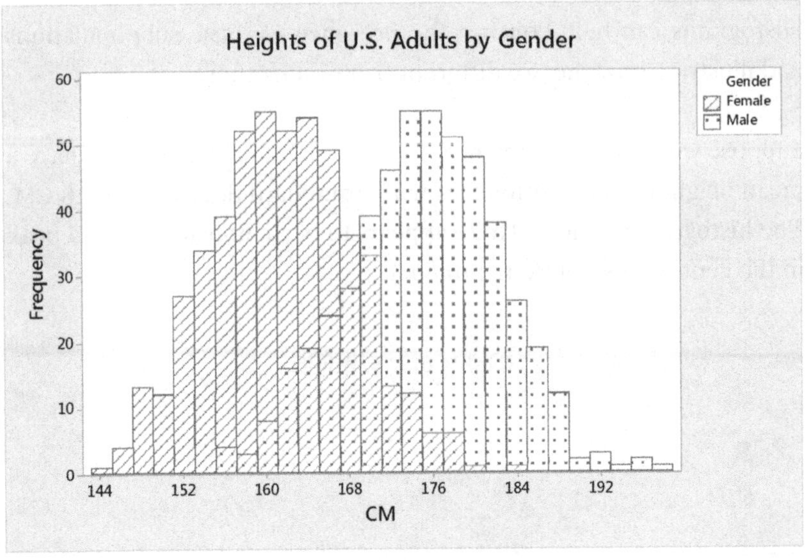

Notice how two narrower distributions have replaced the single broad distribution? The histograms help us learn that gender is an essential categorical variable in studies that involve height. Each gender's distribution clusters more tightly around its central point than the overall distribution around its center. The tighter clustering indicates that the subpopulations provide more precise estimates than the whole population. In this light, the mean for the entire population does not equal the mean for either subpopulation. It's misleading!

In this graph, gender is the categorical variable, and height is the continuous variable. It's an example of contrasting groups in your data to learn about the subject area.

Comparing Distributions between Groups

To compare distributions between groups using histograms, you'll need both a continuous variable and a categorical variable. The categorical variable defines the groups in your data, such as male and female. The continuous variables are measurements. Using a grouping variable in conjunction with continuous data allows you to compare the center and spread of the different distributions.

There are two common ways to display groups in histograms. You can either overlay the groups or graph them in different panels, as shown below.

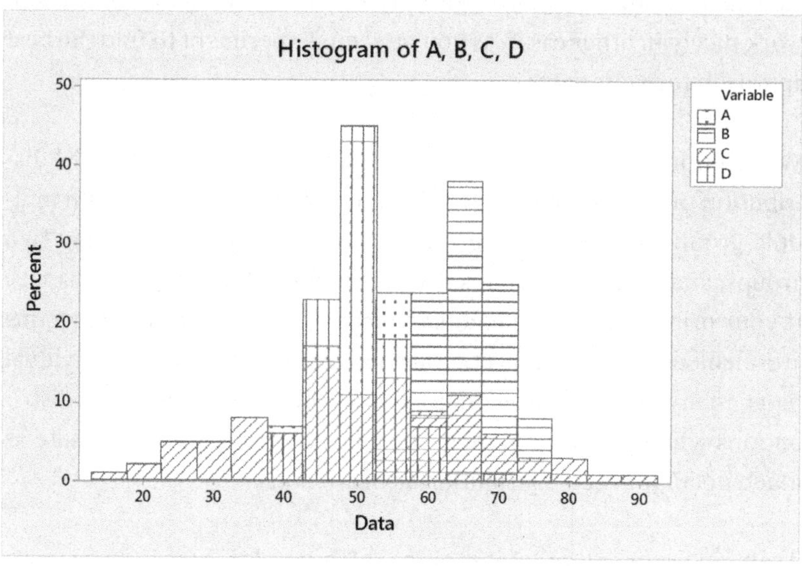

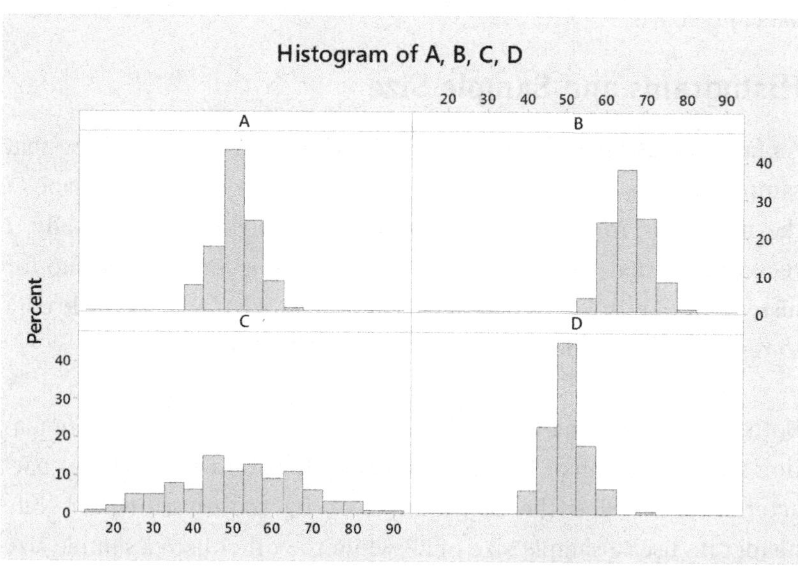

It can be easier to compare distributions when the chart overlays them, but sometimes they get messy. Histograms in separate panels display each distribution more clearly, but the comparisons and degree of overlap aren't quite as clear. In the previous example, the paneled distributions are more legible. However, overlaid histograms can work nicely in other cases, as you've seen. Experiment to find the best approach for your data!

While I think histograms are the best graph for understanding the distribution of values for a single group, they can get muddled with multiple groups. Histograms are usually pretty good for displaying two groups, and up to four groups if you present them in separate panels. If your primary goal is to compare distributions and your histograms are challenging to interpret, consider using boxplots or individual plots. In my opinion, those other plots are better for comparing distributions when you have more groups. But they don't provide quite as much detail for each distribution as histograms.

Again, experiment and determine which graph works best for your data and goals!

Histograms and Sample Size

As fantastic as histograms are for exploring your data, be aware that sample size is a significant consideration when you need the shape of the histogram to resemble the population distribution. Typically, I recommend that you have a sample size of *at least* 20 per group for histograms. With fewer than 20 observations, you have too little data to represent the population distribution accurately.

Both of the following histograms use samples drawn from a population that has a mean of 100 and a standard deviation of 15. These characteristics describe the distribution of IQ scores. However, one histogram uses a sample size of 20 while the other uses a sample size of 100. Notice that I'm using percent on the Y-axis to compare histogram bars between different sample sizes.

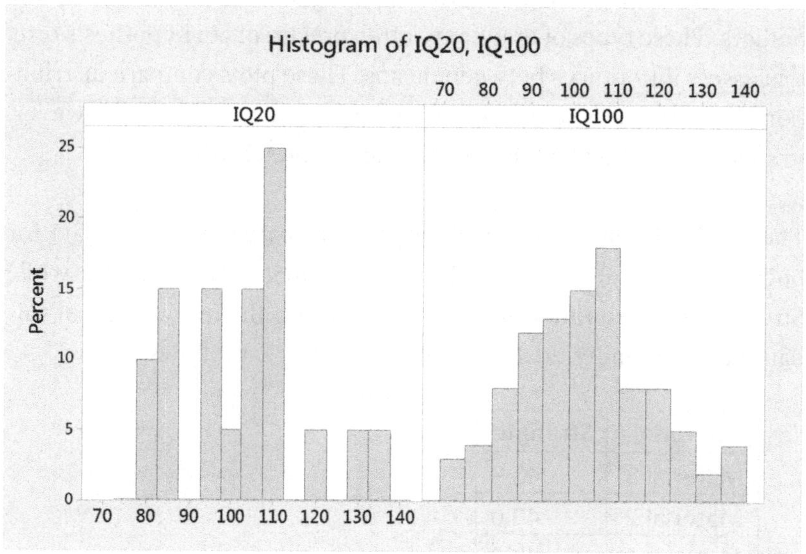

That's a huge difference! It takes a surprisingly large sample size to get a good representation of an entire distribution. When your sample size is less than 20, consider using an individual value plot.

Boxplots vs. Individual Value Plots

Graphing your data before performing statistical analysis is a crucial step. Graphs bring your data to life in a way that statistical measures do not because they display the relationships and patterns. In this section, you'll learn about using boxplots and individual value plots to compare distributions of continuous measurements between groups.

Use boxplots and individual value plots when you have a categorical grouping variable and a continuous outcome variable. The categorical variables form the groups in your data, and the researchers measure the continuous variable. These graphs display relationships between a categorical variable and a continuous variable.

Both graphs allow you to compare the distribution of values between the groups in your sample data. You can assess properties such as the center, spread, and shapes of the distributions while looking out for outliers. These types of graphs are often precursors to hypothesis tests that assess differences between means. These plots compare distributions like the histograms with groups you saw previously. However, in some cases, they highlight differences more clearly.

The partial datasheet below shows how researchers record data for both types of charts. Material is the categorical variable, while Strength is the continuous variable. We'll use the full version of this dataset for the individual value plot example that follows.

Material	Strength
Material 3	41.9
Material 2	40.0
Material 1	42.0
Material 4	44.0
Material 4	40.9
Material 2	43.4

Note that the graphs in this section are best for comparing distributions between groups. When you need to assess a single continuous distribution, histograms are often a better choice.

Individual Value Plots

As the name suggests, individual value plots display the value of each observation. This graph is best when you have fewer than 50 data points per group. With a larger sample size, the data points can become packed close together, jumbled, and hard to evaluate.

- Assess the central tendency by noting the vertical position of each group's center.
- Assess the variability by gauging the vertical range of data points within each group.

Let's take a look at the example below. This chart displays the strengths of four different materials. Material type is our categorical grouping variable, and Strength is the continuous outcome variable that the researchers measured. To create this graph yourself, download the CSV data file from my website: IndividualValuePlot.csv.

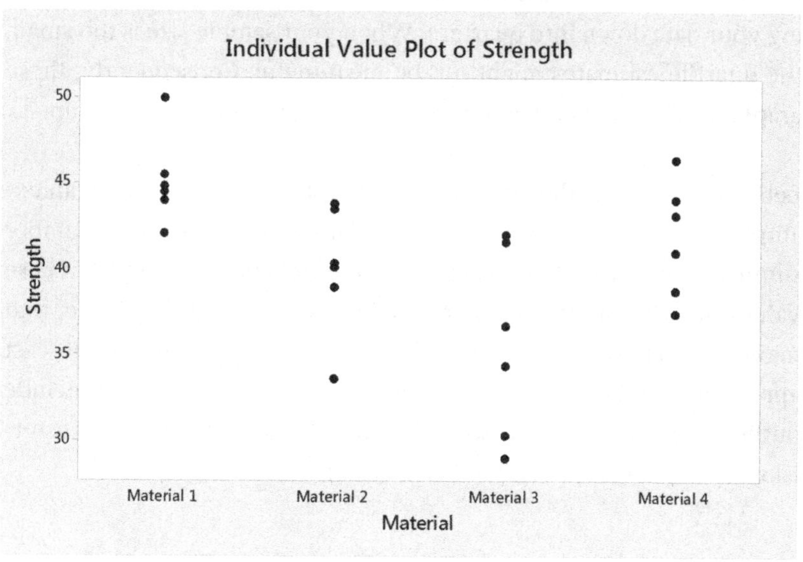

It appears that several different things are happening in this graph. We can compare central tendencies by assessing the overall vertical position of each group. Material 1 has the highest central tendency of the four groups, while Material three has the lowest. Assess variability by looking at the vertical spread of each group's dots. For these data, Material 3 has a broader range than the other groups.

In short, Material 1 has the highest average strength while Material 3 has both the lowest strength and the most variable strength.

Boxplots

Like individual value plots, use boxplots to compare the shapes of distributions, find central tendencies, assess variability, and identify outliers. Boxplots are also known as box and whisker diagrams. While boxplots have the same goals as individual value plots, they look very different.

Instead of displaying the raw data points, boxplots take your sample data and present ranges of values based on quartiles and display asterisks for outliers that fall outside the whiskers. Boxplots work by breaking your data down into quarters. When your sample size is too small, the quartile estimates might not be meaningful. Consequently, these graphs work best when you have at least 20 data points per group.

Let's take a look at the anatomy of a boxplot before getting to an example. Boxplots display what statisticians refer to as a five-number summary, which are five vital descriptive statistics for samples. These values are the minimum, first quartile, median, third quartile, and maximum. These five values divide your data into quarters—at least approximately because the upper and lower whiskers do not include outliers, which the chart displays separately. Outliers display as asterisks beyond the upper and lower whiskers.

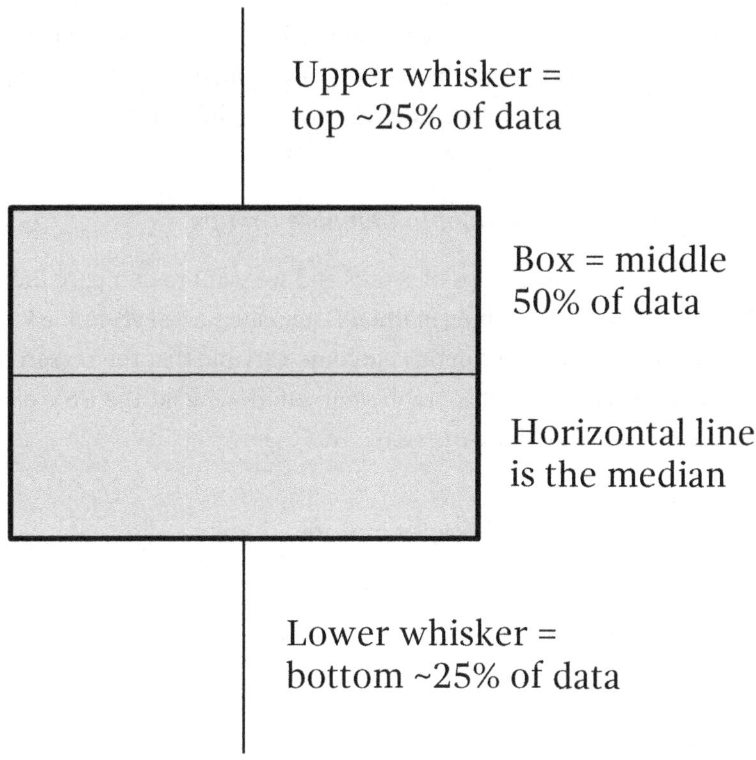

Using Boxplots to Assess Distributions

When you're assessing a single distribution, using a histogram is probably better. However, for comparing multiple distributions, boxplots are an excellent method. I find that they're easier to interpret than individual value plots when you have a sufficiently large sample size.

To compare central tendencies, use the median line in the boxes.

For the variability, remember that half your data for each group falls within the interquartile box. The longer the box and whiskers, the greater the variability of the distribution.

To determine whether a distribution is skewed, look at where the data fall compared to the median. For symmetric distributions, the length of the box and whiskers on both sides of the median should be approximately equal. If the two sides are not roughly equivalent, your distribution is skewed.

Example of Using a Boxplot to Compare Groups

Suppose we have four groups of scores and we want to compare them by teaching method. Teaching method is our categorical grouping variable, and Score is the continuous outcome variable that the researchers measured. To create this graph yourself, download the CSV data file from my website: Boxplot.csv.

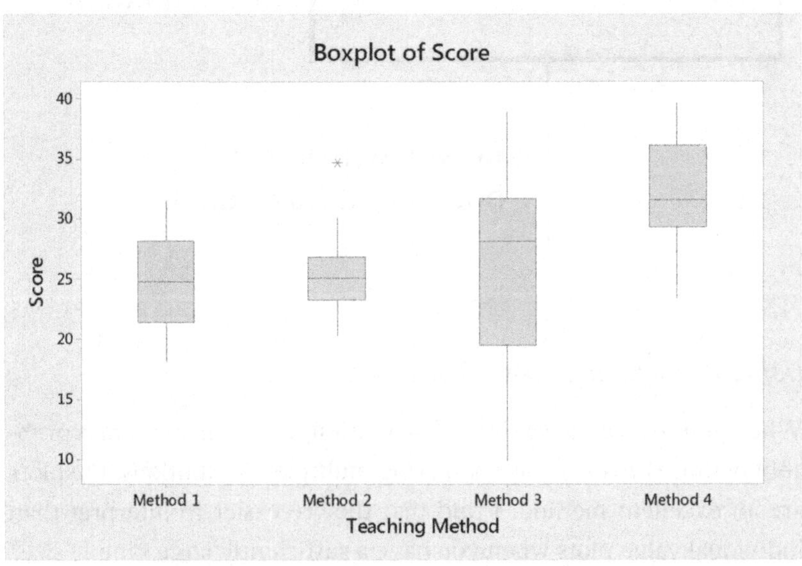

Method 1 and 2 have nearly identical medians, but Method 1 has somewhat more variability. The second method also has an outlier we should investigate. Method 3 has the highest variability in scores and is potentially left-skewed because it has a longer tail going towards lower values. Method 4 has the highest median.

This graph displays the relationship between teaching method and the outcome score. If you know the teaching method, it helps you understand and explain the differences in the scores.

Histograms, individual value plots, and boxplots can contrast the distributions for groups within your dataset. They illustrate relationships between a categorical and continuous variable. However, what do you use when you have a pair of categorical variables? Use two-way contingency tables and bar charts!

Two -Way Contingency Tables

Two-way contingency tables represent the frequency of combinations for two categorical variables. These tables help identify relationships between a pair of categorical variables. You can also graph them using bar charts. Each value in a table cell indicates the number of times researchers observed a particular combination of categorical values.

In the table below, the two categorical variables are gender and ice cream flavor preference. Each cell represents the number of times members of one gender preferred a particular ice cream flavor. The CSV datasheet from my website shows one format you can use to enter the data into your software: Flavor Preference.csv.

Gender	Chocolate	Strawberry	Vanilla	Total
Female	37	17	12	66
Male	21	18	32	71
Total	58	35	44	137

For example, the Female/Chocolate cell indicates that 37 females identified chocolate as their favorite flavor. Conversely, only 21 males liked chocolate ice cream the best.

If there is a relationship between ice cream preference and gender, we'd expect the values in the two gender rows for each flavor to be different. From the table, it appears that females are more likely to prefer chocolate, while males prefer vanilla. Both genders have an equal preference for strawberry. Overall, the table suggests that males and females have different ice cream preferences.

The Total column indicates the researchers surveyed 66 females and 71 males. Because we have roughly equal numbers, we can compare the raw counts directly. However, when you have unequal groups, use percentages to compare them.

For example, the percentage of females who prefer chocolate is simply the number of observations in the Female/Chocolate cell divided by the total number of women (37 / 66 = 56%). We can do the same for males and see that 29.6% (21 / 71) of men prefer chocolate. These two percentages don't add up to 100% because they are row percentages. Each value represents the percentage of each cell out of the total for the row. Consequently, the total for each row sums to 100%--but the columns won't add to 100%.

You can also calculate column percentages. For column percentages, you'd use the total for each column. For example, 58 subjects preferred chocolate. Of those who prefer chocolate, 63% are women (37 / 58) and 36% (21 / 58) are men. Use row and/or column percentages as they make sense for your analysis.

The next table uses the same raw data as the previous contingency table, but it also displays both row and column percentages. Note how the row percentages sum to 100% while the column percentages sum to 100%.

Gender	Chocolate	Strawberry	Vanilla	Row Total
Female	Raw: 37 Row%: 56% Col%: 63.8%	Raw: 17 Row%: 25.8% Col%: 48.6%	Raw: 12 Row%: 18.2% Col%: 28.8%	Raw: 66 Row%: 100%
Male	Raw: 21 Row%:29.6% Col%: 36.2%	Raw: 18 Row%: 25.4% Col%: 51.4%	Raw: 32 Row%: 45.0% Col%: 71.2%	Raw: 71 Row%: 100%
Total	Raw: 58 Col%: 100%	Raw: 35 Col%: 100%	Raw: 44 Col%: 100%	137

Using percentages is crucial when groups sizes aren't equal. Focusing on row percentages or column percentages depends on the question you want to answer. In our case, we want to know whether flavor preference depends on gender. Because the two genders display in separate rows, we'll look for differences in the row percentages.

You can also use bar charts to display the results of a contingency table. The following clustered bar chart displays the row percentages for the previous table. I've set the graph to cluster the female and male pairs of bars together for each flavor, which makes comparisons easier. I think it gives a nice oomph to the tabular results.

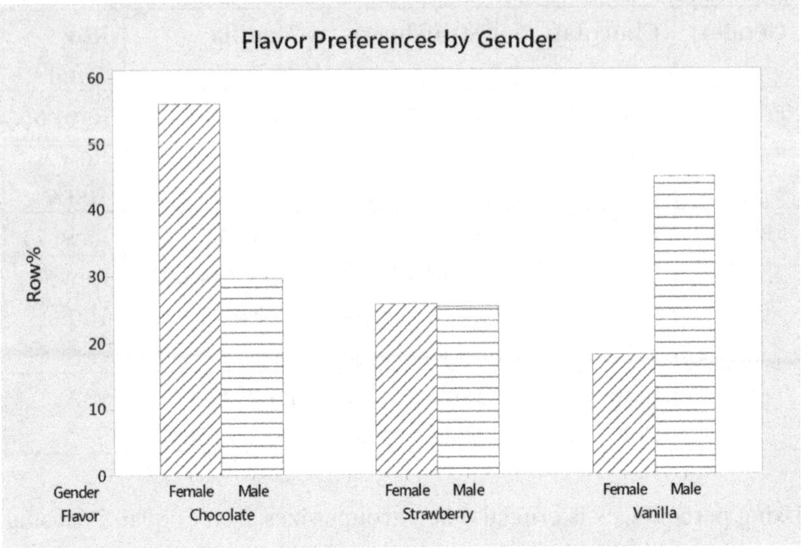

This bar chart reiterates our conclusions from the first contingency table. Women in this sample prefer chocolate, men favor vanilla, and both genders have an equal preference for strawberry.

Cautions About Graphing

I'm sure you can tell that I love graphs! When you want a good, intuitive view of the data, graphs are great choices. However, I have two cautions about them.

Manipulating Graphs

Graphs are subject to manipulation. There might even be good motivations behind the manipulation, such as making it look more dramatic. By changing aspects like the axes, or bin sizes on histograms, you can change the appearance of graphs substantially. The same data can look very different and seem to convey different interpretations.

For example, the relationships in the following two scatterplots look very different. However, they're displaying the same data. The first graph is more dramatic.

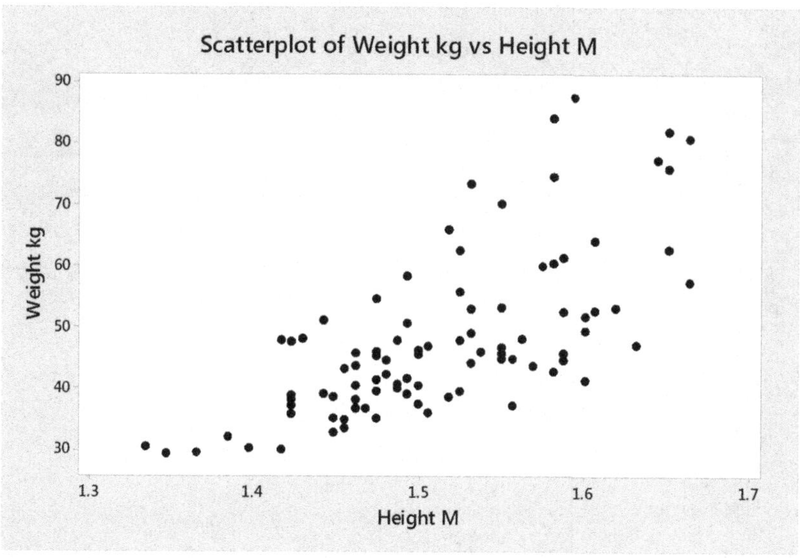

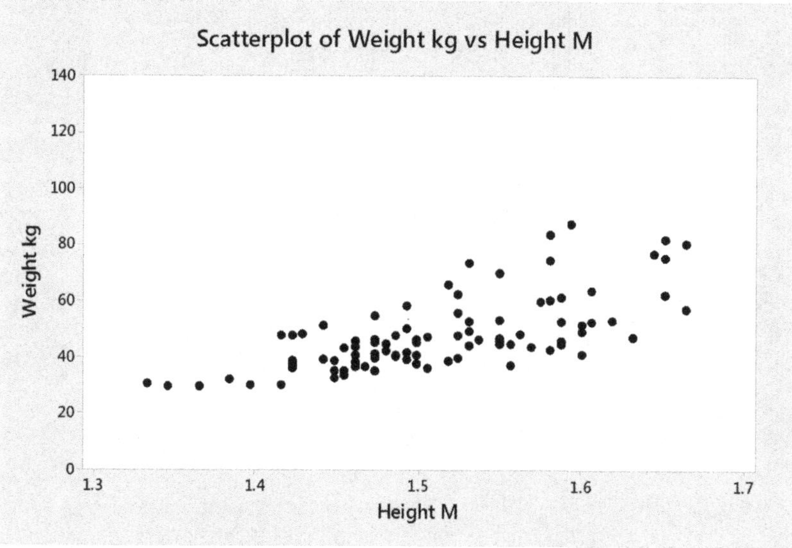

The following two boxplots also display the same dataset. The difference between the two groups appears more significant in the first plot.

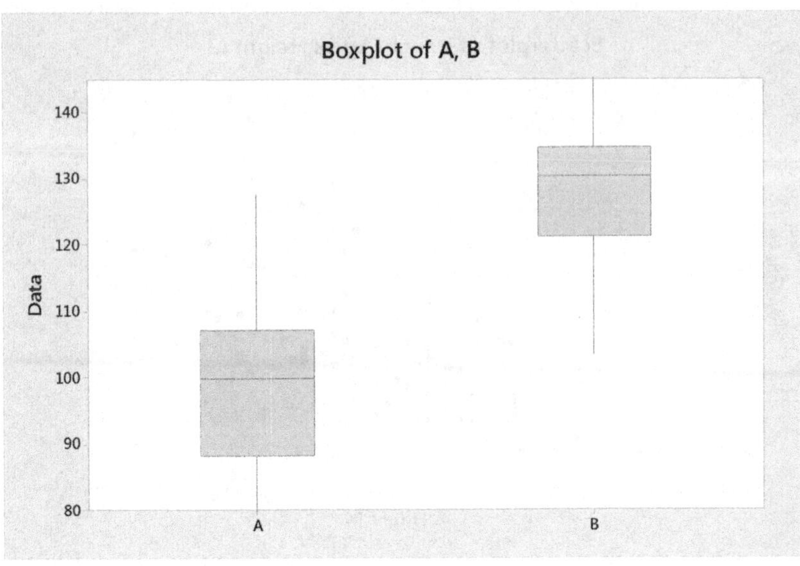

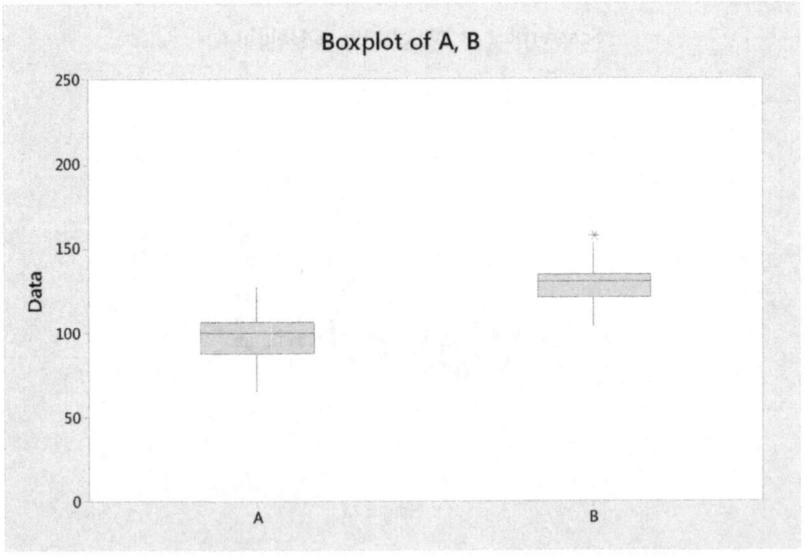

Anytime you look at a graph, carefully evaluate the scales!

Numeric measures are more objective and not as easy to manipulate. Correlation coefficients and the difference between means don't change based on the graph's axes! That's why I'll often use summary statistics and graphs together.

Drawing Inferences About a Population Requires Additional Testing

Graphs can help identify relationships in the data. You've seen examples of relationships between different types of variables.

Graphs are excellent tools for bringing all of these relationships to life visually. However, if your goal is to use the sample to estimate relationships in a population, you'll need to use a hypothesis test. There are other requirements as well, which we'll explore later in the book.

Hypothesis testing is beyond the scope of this book. In broad strokes, these tests determine whether relationships in your sample data are likely to exist in the population. The patterns you see in the graphs might be flukes based on random sampling error rather than denoting a real relationship in the population. Hypothesis tests play a critical role in separating the signal (real effects in the population) from the noise (random sampling error). This protective function helps prevent you from mistaking random error for a real effect.

Chapter 5 discusses many of these topics, including inferential statistics, representative sampling, populations, and random sampling error. For now, understand that seeing patterns in graphs requires follow-up tests when you want to use a sample to estimate relationships in a population.

We'll close this chapter with a bit of fun about changing the axes on graphs. It's fun, but there's a good point behind it all!

Graphing and Philosophy

As my family and I were being rattled around in a four-wheel drive vehicle in the remote Osa Peninsula in Costa Rica, it struck me that traveling to exotic locations is just like manually adjusting the scales on graphs! That's probably not what you were expecting, but let me explain!

We love to travel. My family and I particularly enjoy traveling abroad. For us, you just can't beat experiencing new customs, cultures, sights, and food. In fact, we joke that we have a case of chronic travel itch! The experiences and memories are priceless and last a lifetime.

One of our favorite places is Costa Rica. We have hiked through rainforests, cloud forests, and up a volcano! In the process, we saw many tropical birds, monkeys, colorful frogs, snakes, and reptiles. On a night hike through the rainforest, we saw the deadliest snake in Costa Rica, the Bothrops asper. Our favorite place to stay is an ecolodge where we stay in a hut in the middle of the rainforest!

What I realized during that bouncy ride is that travel provides a new perspective on life, just like adjusting the scales on graphs provides a new view of data.

Automatic versus Manual Graph Scales

I'll explain this concept using the idea of a local view and a global view. When we were shopping for a new car, the salesman emphasized the smooth ride. Rough rides can be annoying. At that time, we were near home and just comparing the journey in the context of the smooth local roads.

Those bumps were on a vastly different scale than the bumps on the rough road in remote Costa Rica. This contrast still makes me smile because we loved that fun ride in Costa Rica. Perhaps it's not so important to eliminate all of the bumps from your life? That's an important realization right there!

Let's graph the intensity of the bumps near home and the bumps in the jungle on time series plots. When you use automatic scaling in statistical software, the data fill the plot in a pleasant, visually appealing manner. I consider this the local view of your data. The data you measure fill your entire perspective. The graph is not taking a broader perspective from outside the data into account. That's like when you're near home, and your daily life fills your entire view.

The next two graphs look reasonably similar because they each use the automatically generated scale. The data fill the charts perfectly. Each one seems nice and normal. It's that comfortable feeling of familiar surroundings.

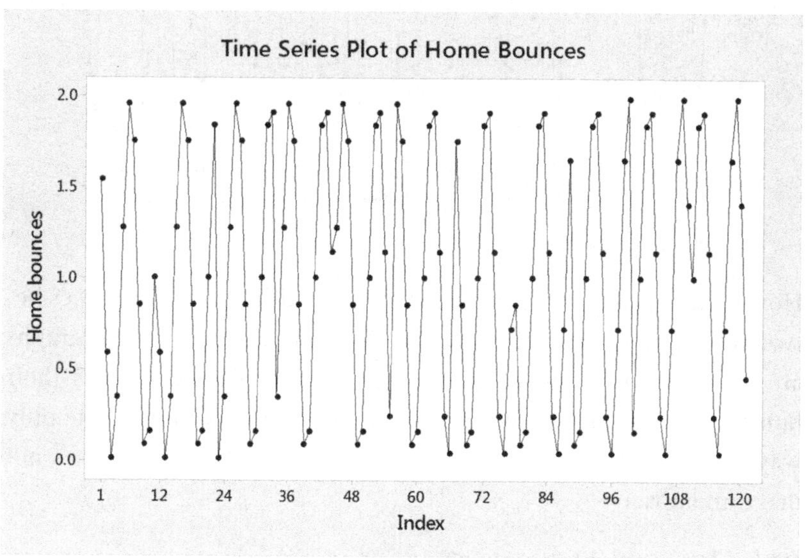

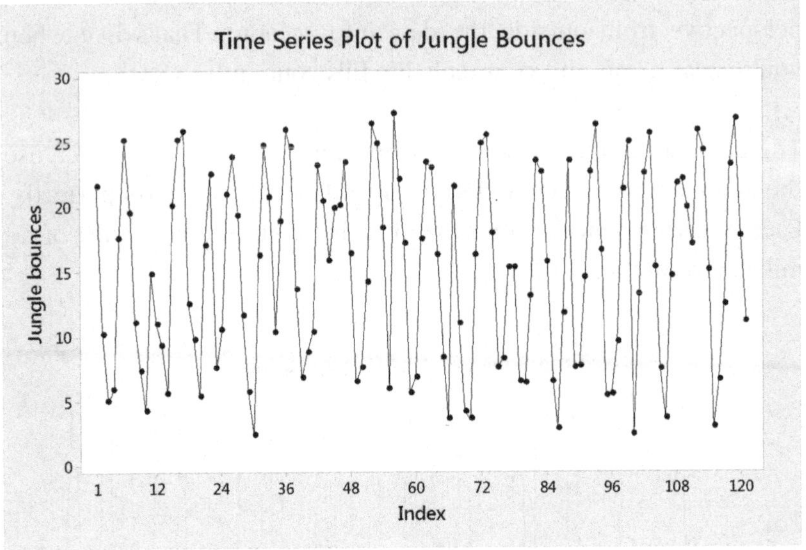

However, the similarity disguises the vastly different experiences between the bumps near home versus those in the jungle! These graphs are analogous to how a local person in each place considers their bumps to be normal. Looking at the y-axes very carefully is the only way to notice the different scaling. Visually, the difference does not make an impact.

When You Should Change Graph Scales

Ideally, a chart should make differences in the data visually apparent. In the case of the roads, having traveled roads in both places, it was easy for me to compare them mentally. I used the broader perspective gained by going to the rainforest and applied it to my experiences at home.

To do this with graphs, you need to adjust the scales manually. I'll use the scale from the Jungle Bounces graph and apply it to my Home Bounces graph. The chart uses the same home data but with the new y-axis scale.

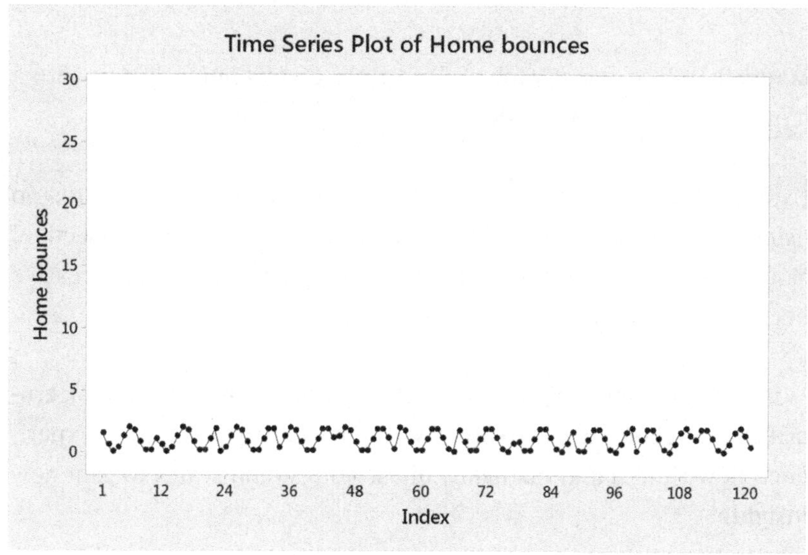

This graph might look awkward or odd. All of the data are jammed down at the bottom with a large unused area above. However, it certainly brings the difference to life! It makes an impact.

That, my friends, is what traveling is all about. You might feel a bit awkward or uncomfortable in a very different setting, but the new perspective makes an impact on you!

Don't Limit Yourself by Always Using Automatic Scaling

In our daily lives, our minds construct a world view using something like automatic scaling. Whatever we experience regularly becomes the picture that fills our perspective. It's what we consider normal. Everything gets neatly resized to fit the mental box—just like those first two graphs.

The upside is that it produces that comfortable feeling. However, it's also limiting because it doesn't let you see the full picture.

Travel to put your life data into a broader context and learn by comparison.

Manually adjust your graph scales to place your numeric data into a larger context and make the graphs easier to compare.

Exploring new environments and cultures is a fantastic way to stop using your mind's automatic scaling and obtain a new perspective! You'll learn new things, feel energized, and possibly be more creative because you can draw upon a broader range of experiences.

With this broader context, you might find that things which look crucial at first glance are actually trivial. Or vice versa. Explore, experience new things, and manually adjust your graph scales to gain new insights!

Summary and Next Steps

This chapter covered the different types of data and how to graph them. In particular, you learned how to use graphs to understand the properties of the dataset and to look for relationships between different types of variables.

Type	You can assess
Continuous	Infinite number of values between any two points. Assess differences between values (intervals), and sometimes ratios. Spread, center, skew.
Discrete	Counts. Nonnegative integers. Similar to continuous. However, cannot divide them into smaller components. Finite number of points between two values.
Categorical	Finite number of values that do not have an order. No distances between values. Counts and percentages of values.
Binary	Categorical data with only two values.
Ordinal	Categorical data with a natural order. No fixed distances between values.

We also learned how various graphs can help us explore the properties of different data types.

Graph	Goals and Data
Scatterplots	Assess the relationship between pairs of continuous variables.
Time series plot	Assess changes in continuous variables over time.
Histogram	Assess distribution properties of a continuous variable. Optionally, include a categorical variable that defines groups to compare distributions.
Boxplots	Assess distribution properties of a continuous variable. Typically, include a categorical variable that defines groups to compare distributions. Larger datasets are better.
Individual value plots	Assess distribution properties of a continuous variable. Optionally, include a categorical variable that defines groups to compare distributions. Smaller datasets are better.
Bar charts	Compare counts or proportions of discrete, categorical, binary, and ordinal data.
Pie charts	Show proportions of a whole for categorical, binary, and ordinal data.

The process of setting up contrasts between groups in your data and seeing how the values of one variable depend on the value of another is a fundamental building block of identifying relationships and designing experiments. We'll explore that in much more detail later in the book.

Graphs provide an intuitive view of your dataset, but there are several cautions about using them.

- Scaling can either amplify or diminish the appearance of relationships between variables.
- Making inferences about a population requires a hypothesis test.

While this chapter focused on graphical representations of datasets and relationships, the next chapter details numeric measures of these properties.

CHAPTER 3

Summary Statistics and Relative Standing

So far, we've looked at the big-picture view of the field of statistics, learned about the different types of data, how to graph them, and using graphs to describe datasets and find relationships. Graphs summarize a dataset visually. Now we'll move on to summarizing datasets with numbers.

A summary statistic is a number derived from a dataset that summarizes a property of the entire dataset. There are four categories of summary statistics:

- Measures of central tendency or location, such as the mean.
- Measures of spread or dispersion, such as the standard deviation.
- Measures of correlation or dependency, such as Pearson's correlation coefficient.
- Measures of the shape of a distribution, such as skewness or thickness of the tails.

In this chapter, we'll go over the first three. Summary statistics about the shape of a distribution are not used as commonly and generally not covered in basic statistics.

For good measure, you'll also learn about percentiles, which measures the relative standing of an observation. Technically, it's not a summary statistic, but it does indicate where a particular observation falls relative to the entire dataset. Although, as you'll see, you can also use percentiles as a measure of central tendency and a measure of variability.

In the previous chapter, I described how graphs provide a more intuitive feel for your data. I highly recommend using charts to explore your data and get a real sense for what it is saying. However, as you saw at the end of the chapter, graphs can give the wrong impression when analysts or the software change the axes' scaling. These problems are particularly prevalent when you're comparing groups or assessing correlations between variables.

Summary statistics help avoid these problems by providing an objective number. For example, the difference between group means and the correlation coefficient for a pair of variables do not change when you adjust the scales of a graph. They are what they are because they use a consistent calculation method.

Percentiles

Percentiles are a great tool to use when you need to know the relative standing of a value. Where does a value fall within a distribution of values? While the concept behind percentiles is straight forward, there are different mathematical methods for calculating them. In this section, learn about percentiles, special percentiles and their surprisingly flexible uses, and the various procedures for calculating them.

Percentiles tell you how a value compares to other values. The general rule is that if value X is at the kth percentile, then X is greater than K%

of the values. Let's see how this information can be helpful. For example, a person with an IQ of 120 is at the 91st percentile, which indicates that their IQ is higher than 91 percent of other scores.

Often the units for raw test scores are not informative. When you obtain a score on the SAT, ACT, or GRE, the units are meaningless by themselves. A total SAT score of 1340 is not inherently meaningful. Instead, you really want to know the percentage of test-takers that you scored better than. For the SAT, a total score of 1340 is approximately the 90th percentile. Congratulations, you scored better than 90% of the other test-takers. Only 10% scored better than you. Now that's helpful!

Sometimes measurement units are meaningful, but you still would like to know the relative standing. For example, if your one-month-old baby weighs five kilograms, you might wonder how that weight compares to other babies. For a one-month old baby girl, that equates to the 77th percentile. Your little girl weighs more than 77% of other girls her age, while 23% weigh more than her. You know right where she fits in with her cohort!

Special Percentiles

We give names to particular percentiles. The 50th percentile is the median. This value splits a dataset in half. Half the values are below the 50th percentile, and half are above it. The median is a measure of central tendency in statistics.

Quartiles are values that divide your data into quarters, and they are based on percentiles.

- The first quartile, also known as Q1 or the lower quartile, is the value of the 25th percentile. The bottom quarter of the scores fall below this value, while three-quarters fall above it.
- The second quartile, also known as Q2 or the median, is the value of the 50th percentile. Half the scores are above and half below.
- The third quartile, also known as Q3 or the upper quartile, is the value of the 75% percentile. The top quarter of the scores fall above this value, while three-quarters fall below it.

The interquartile range (IQR) is a measure of dispersion in statistics. This range corresponds to the distance between the first quartile and the third quartile (IQR = Q3 – Q1). Larger IQRs indicate that the data are more spread out. The interquartile range represents the middle half of the data. One-quarter of the values fall below the IQR while another quarter of the values are above it.

Percentiles are surprisingly versatile because you can use them purposes other than just obtaining a relative standing. They can also divide your dataset into portions, identify the central tendency, and measure the dispersion of a distribution. We'll cover these other uses throughout this chapter.

Calculating Percentiles Using Values in a Dataset

Percentile is a fairly common word. Surprisingly, there isn't a single standard definition for it. Consequently, there are multiple methods for calculating percentiles. In this chapter, I'll cover three methods that analysts use to calculate percentiles when looking at the actual data values in a dataset. In chapter 4, I show how to calculate percentiles using probability distributions.

The three calculation methods define the kth percentile in the following slightly different ways:

- The smallest value that is greater than k percent of the values.
- The smallest value that is greater than or equal to k percent of values.
- An interpolated value between the two closest ranks.

While the first two definitions might not seem drastically different, they can produce significantly different results, particularly when you are working with a small dataset. As you will see, this difference occurs because the first two definitions use different ranks that correspond to different scores. The third definition mitigates this concern by interpolating between two ranks to estimate a percentile value that falls between two values.

To calculate percentiles using these three approaches, start by ranking your dataset from the lowest to highest values.

Let's use these three methods with the following dataset (n=11) to find the 70th percentile.

Rank	Value
1	2
2	4
3	6
4	8
5	13
6	16
7	22
8	35
9	40
10	42
11	48

Definition 1: Greater Than

Using the first definition, we need to find the value that is greater than 70% of the values, and there are 11 values. Take 70% of 11, which is 7.7. Then, round 7.7 up to 8. Using the first definition, the value for the 70th percentile must be greater than eight values. Consequently, we pick the 9th ranked value in the dataset, which is 40.

Definition 2: Greater Than or Equal To

Using the second definition, we need to find the value that is greater than or equal to 70% of the values. Thanks to the "equal to" portion of the definition, we can use the 8th ranked value, which is 35.

Using the first two definitions, we have found two values for the 70% percentile—35 and 40.

Definition 3: Using an Interpolation Approach

As you saw, using either "greater" or "greater than or equal to" changes the results. Depending on the nature and size of your dataset, this difference can be substantial. Consequently, a third approach interpolates between two data values.

To calculate an interpolated percentile, do the following:

1. Calculate the rank to use for the percentile. Use: rank = p(n+1), where p = the percentile and n = the sample size. For our example, to find the rank for the 70th percentile, we take 0.7*(11 + 1) = 8.4.
2. If the rank in step 1 is an integer, find the data value that corresponds to that rank and use it for the percentile.
3. If the rank is not an integer, you need to interpolate between the two closest observations. For our example, 8.4 falls between 8 and 9, which corresponds to the data values of 35 and 40.

4. Take the difference between these two observations and multiply it by the fractional portion of the rank. For our example, this is: (40 – 35)0.4 = 2.
5. Take the lower-ranked value in step 3 and add the value from step 4 to obtain the interpolated value for the percentile. For our example, that value is 35 + 2 = 37.

Using three standard calculations for percentiles, we find three different values for the 70th percentile: 35, 37, and 40.

Percentiles are a very intuitive way to understand where a value falls within a distribution of values. However, if you need to calculate a percentile, you'll need to decide which method to use!

Measures of Central Tendency

A measure of central tendency is a summary statistic that represents the center point or typical value of a dataset. These measures indicate where most values in a distribution fall. In other words, it's the central location of a distribution. You can think of it as the tendency of data to cluster around a middle value. In statistics, the three most common measures of central tendency are the mean, median, and mode. Each of these measures calculates the location of the central point using a different method.

Choosing the best measure of central tendency depends on the type of data you have. In this section, I explore these measures of central tendency, show you how to calculate them, and how to determine which one is best for your data.

Most texts you'll read about the mean, median, and mode focus on how you calculate each one—and I'll get to that as well. However, I'm going to start with a slightly different approach. My philosophy is to help you intuitively grasp statistics by focusing on concepts. Consequently, I'm going to start by illustrating the central point of several datasets graphically—so you understand the goal. Then, we'll move on to choosing the best measure of central tendency for your data and the calculations.

The following three distributions represent different data conditions. In each distribution, look for the region where the most common values fall. Even though the shapes and type of data are different, you can find that central location. That's the area in the distribution where the most common values are located.

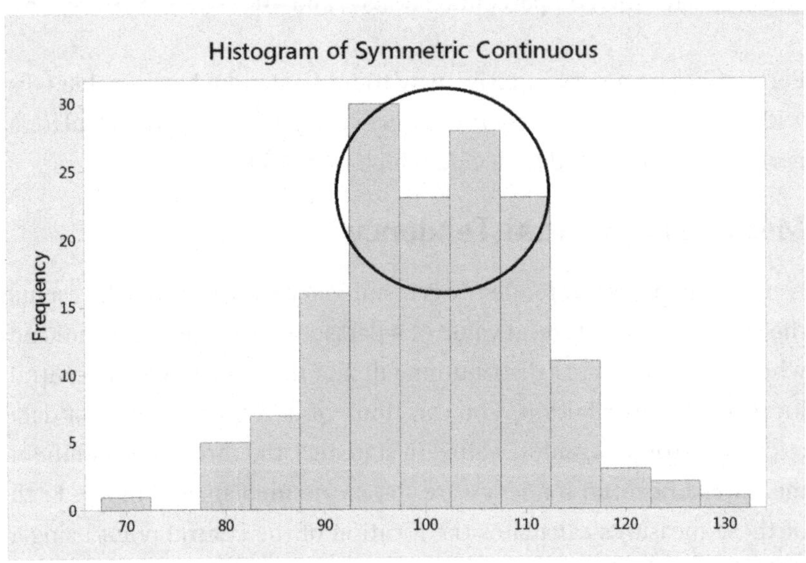

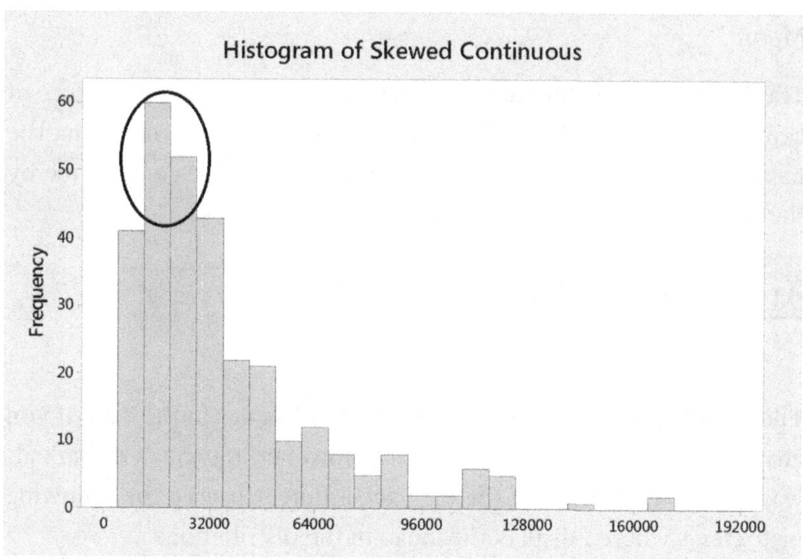

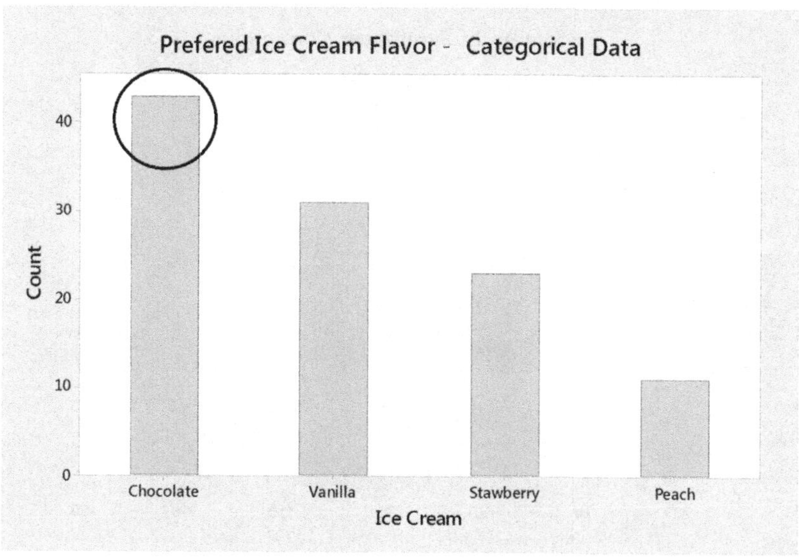

As the graphs highlight, you can see where most values tend to occur. That's the concept. Measures of central tendency represent this idea with a value. Coming up, you'll learn that as the distribution and type of data changes, so does the best measure of central tendency. Consequently, you need to know the kind of data you have, and graph it, before choosing a measure of central tendency!

Mean

The mean is the arithmetic average, and it is probably the measure of central tendency with which you are most familiar. Calculating the mean is very simple. You just add up all of the values and divide by the number of observations in your dataset.

$$\frac{X_1 + X_2 + \cdots + X_n}{n}$$

The calculation of the mean incorporates all values in the data. If you change any value, the mean changes. However, the mean doesn't always locate the center of the data accurately. Observe the following histograms where I display the mean in the distributions.

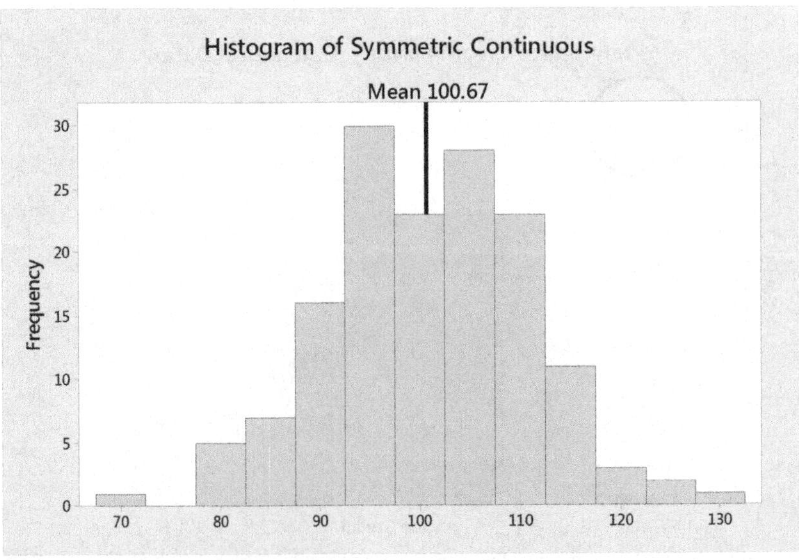

In a symmetric distribution, the mean locates the center accurately.

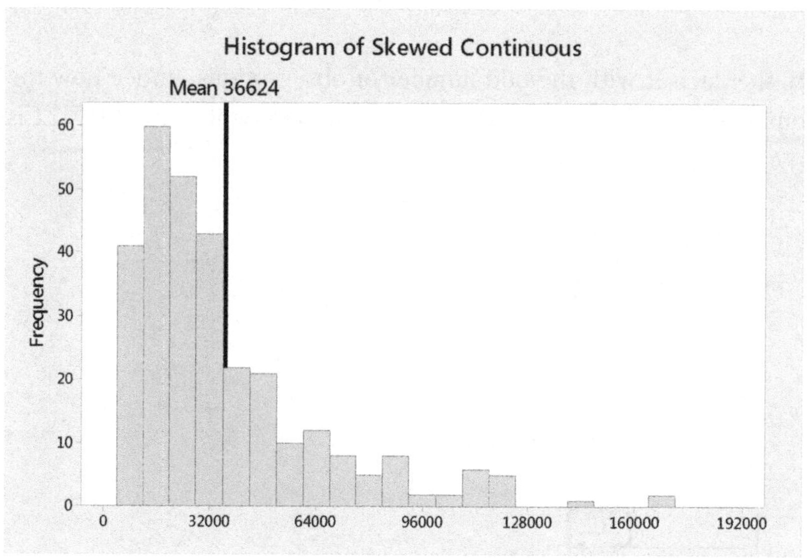

However, in a skewed distribution, the mean can miss the mark. In the histogram above, it starts to fall outside the central area. This problem occurs because outliers have a substantial impact on the mean. Extreme values in an extended tail pull the mean away from the center. As the distribution becomes more skewed, the mean is drawn further away from the center. Consequently, it's best to use the mean as a measure of the central tendency when you have a symmetric distribution.

When to use the mean: Symmetric distribution, Continuous data

Median

The median is the middle value. It is the value that splits the dataset in half. To find the median, order your data from smallest to largest, and then find the data point that has an equal amount of values above it and below it. The method for locating the median varies slightly depending on whether you have an even or odd number of values. I'll show you how to find the median for both cases. In the following examples, I use whole numbers for simplicity, but you can have decimal places.

In the dataset with the odd number of observations, notice how the number 12 has six values above it and six below it. Therefore, 12 is the median of this dataset.

Median Odd
23
21
18
16
15
13
12
10
9
7
6
5
2

When there is an even number of values, you count in to the two innermost values and then take the average. The average of 27 and 29 is 28. Consequently, 28 is the median of this dataset.

Median Even
40
38
35
33
32
30
29
27
26
24
23
22
19
17

28

Outliers and skewed data have a smaller effect on the median. To understand why, imagine we have the following Median dataset and find that the median is 46. However, we discover data entry errors and need to change four values, which I've bolded in the Median Fixed dataset. We'll make all the changes significantly higher, causing the distribution to become highly skewed with large outliers.

Median	Median Fixed
69	**112**
56	**93**
54	**89**
52	**82**
47	47
46	46
46	46
45	45
43	43
36	36
35	35
34	34
31	31

As you can see, the median doesn't change at all. It is still 46. Unlike the mean, the median value doesn't depend on all the values in the dataset. Consequently, when some of the values are more extreme, the effect on the median is smaller. Of course, with other types of changes, the median can change. When you have a skewed distribution, the median is a better measure of central tendency than the mean.

Comparing the mean and median

Now, let's test the median on the symmetrical and skewed distributions to see how it performs, and I'll include the mean on the histograms so we can compare them.

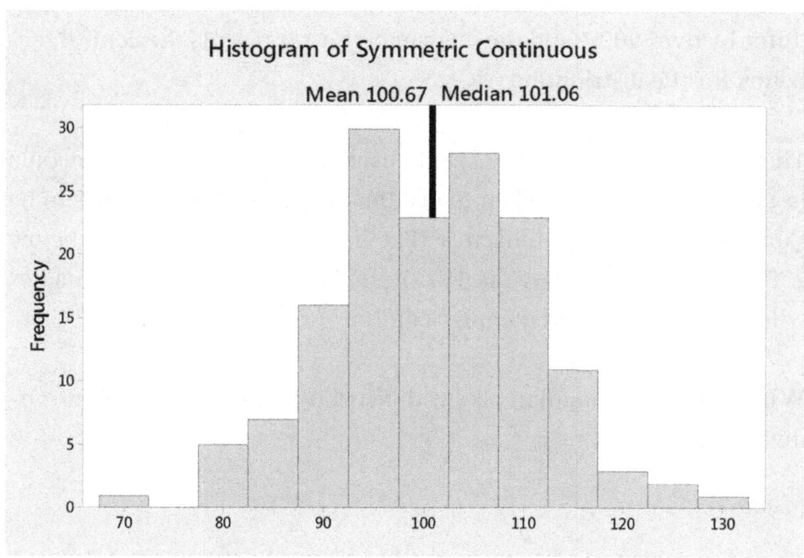

In a symmetric distribution, the mean and median both find the center accurately. They are approximately equal.

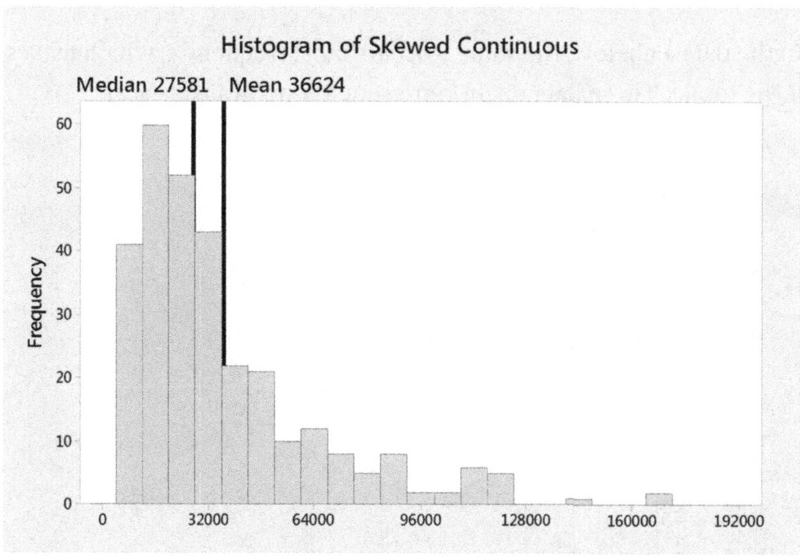

In skewed distributions, outliers in the tail pull the mean from the center towards the longer tail. For this example, the mean and median differ by over 9000, and the median better represents the central tendency for the distribution.

These data are based on the U.S. household income for 2006. Income is a classic example of when to use the median because it tends to be skewed. The median indicates that half of all incomes fall below 27581, and half are above it. For these data, the mean overestimates where most household incomes fall.

When to use the median: Skewed distribution, Continuous data, Ordinal data

Mode

The mode is the value that occurs the most frequently in your data set. On a bar chart, the mode is the highest bar. When the data have multiple values that tie for occurring most often, you have a multimodal distribution. If no value repeats, the data do not have a mode.

In the dataset below, the value 5 occurs most frequently, which makes it the mode. These data might represent a 5-point Likert scale.

Mode
5
5
5
4
4
3
2
2
1

Typically, you use the mode with categorical, ordinal, and discrete data. In fact, the mode is the only measure of central tendency that you can use with categorical data—such as the most preferred flavor of ice cream. However, with categorical data, there isn't a central value because you can't order the groups. With ordinal and discrete data, the mode can be a value that is not in the center. Again, the mode represents the most common value.

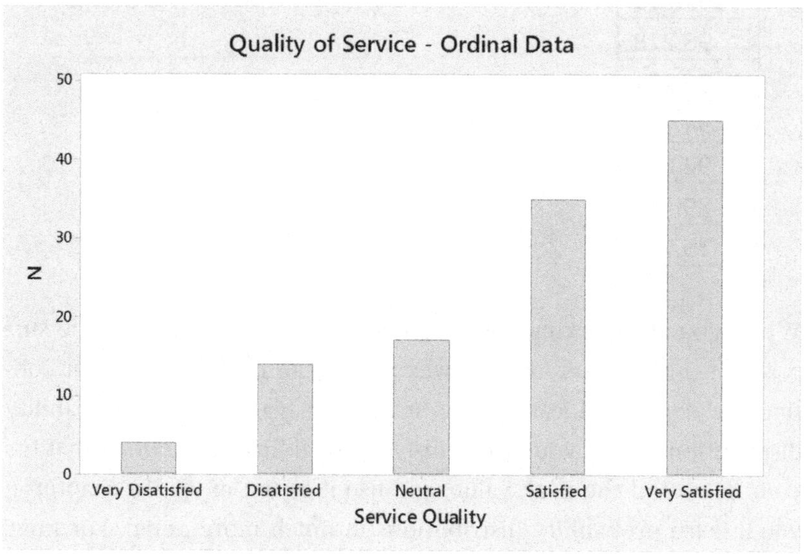

In the graph of service quality, Very Satisfied is the mode of this distribution because it is the most common value in the data. Notice how it is at the extreme end of the distribution. I'm sure the service providers are pleased with these results!

Finding the mode for continuous data

In the continuous data below, no values repeat, which means there is no mode. With continuous data, it is unlikely that two or more values will be exactly equal because there are an infinite number of values between any two values.

No Mode
122.275
109.085
103.079
102.691
98.228
96.221
94.724
92.619
89.483
75.762

When you are working with the raw continuous data, don't be surprised if there is no mode. However, you can find the mode for continuous data by locating the maximum value on a probability distribution plot. If you can identify a probability distribution that fits your data, find the peak value, and use it as the mode. In chapter 4, you'll learn probability distributions in much more detail. For now, just note that probability distribution plots are the best way to find a mode for continuous data.

The probability distribution plot displays a lognormal distribution that has a mode of 16700. This distribution corresponds to the U.S. household income example in the median section.

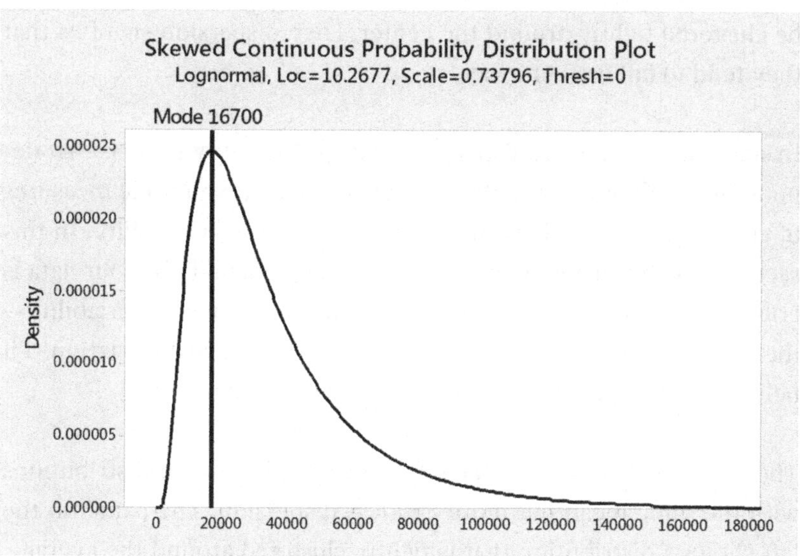

When to use the mode: Categorical data, Ordinal data, Count data, Probability Distributions

Which One to Use?

When you have a symmetrical distribution for continuous data, the mean, median, and mode are equal. In this case, analysts tend to use the mean because it includes all of the data in the calculations. However, if you have a skewed distribution, the median is often the best measure of central tendency.

When you have ordinal data, the median or mode is usually the best choice. For categorical data, you have to use the mode.

Measures of Variability

A measure of variability is a summary statistic that represents the amount of dispersion in a dataset. How spread out are the values? While a measure of central tendency describes the typical value, measures of variability define how far away the data points tend to fall from the center. We talk about variability in the context of a distribution of values. A low dispersion indicates that the data points tend to be clustered tightly around the center. High dispersion signifies that they tend to fall further away.

In statistics, variability, dispersion, and spread are synonyms that denote the width of the distribution. Just as there are multiple measures of central tendency, there are several measures of variability. In this section, you'll learn why understanding the variability of your data is critical. Then, I explore the most common measures of variability—the range, interquartile range, variance, and standard deviation. I'll help you determine which one is best for your data.

The two plots below show the difference graphically for distributions with the same mean but more and less dispersion. The panel on the left shows a distribution that is tightly clustered around the average, while the distribution in the right panel is more spread out.

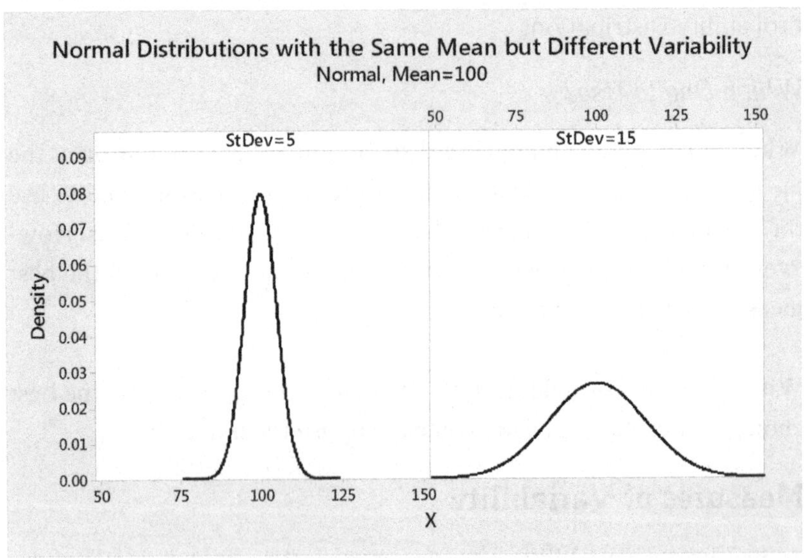

Why Understanding Variability is Important

Let's take a step back and first get a handle on why understanding variability is so essential. Analysts frequently use the mean to summarize the center of a population or a process. While the mean is relevant, people often react to variability even more. When a distribution has lower variability, the values in a dataset are more consistent. However, when the variability is higher, the data points are more dissimilar and extreme values become more likely. Consequently, understanding variability helps you grasp the likelihood of unusual events.

In some situations, extreme values can cause problems! Have you seen a weather report where the meteorologist shows extreme heat and drought in one area and flooding in another? It would be nice to average those together! Frequently, we feel discomfort at the extremes more than the mean. Understanding that variability around the mean provides critical information.

Variability is everywhere. Your commute time to work varies a bit every day. When you order a favorite dish at a restaurant repeatedly, it isn't exactly the same each time. The parts that come off an assembly line might appear to be identical, but they have subtly different lengths and widths.

These are all examples of real-life variability. Some degree of variation is unavoidable. However, too much inconsistency can cause problems. If your morning commute takes much longer than the mean travel time, you will be late for work. If the restaurant dish is much different than how it is usually, you might not like it at all. And, if a manufactured part is too much out of spec, it won't function as intended.

Distributions with greater variability produce observations with unusually large and small values more frequently than distributions with less variability.

Example of Different Amounts of Variability

Let's take a look at two hypothetical pizza restaurants. They both advertise a mean delivery time of 20 minutes. When we're ravenous, they sound equally good! However, this equivalence can be deceptive!

To determine the restaurant that you should order from when you're hungry, we need to analyze their variability.

Suppose we study their delivery times, calculate the variability for each place, and determine that their variation is different. We've computed the standard deviations for both restaurants—which is a measure we'll come back to later. How significant is this difference in getting pizza to their customers promptly?

The graphs below display the distribution of delivery times and provide the answer. The restaurant with more variable delivery times has a broader distribution curve. I've used the same scales in both graphs so you can visually compare the two distributions.

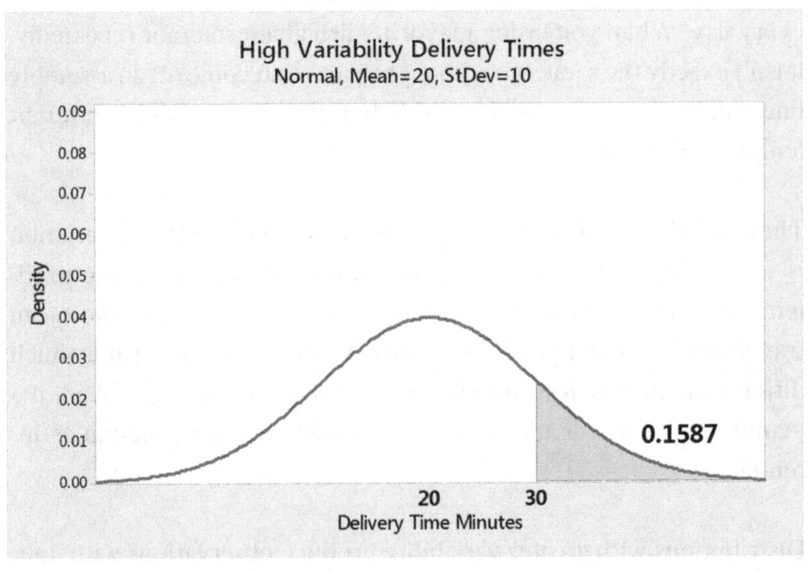

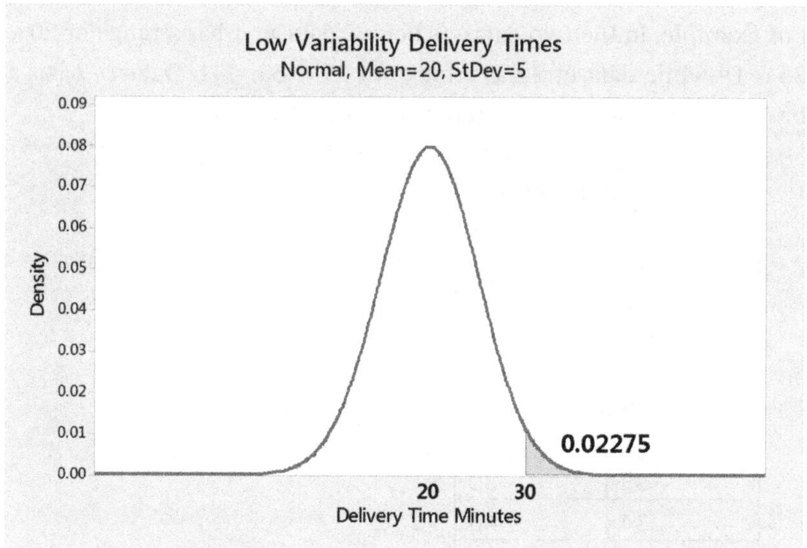

In these graphs, we consider a 30-minute wait or longer to be unacceptable. We're hungry after all! The shaded area in each chart represents the proportion of delivery times that surpass 30 minutes. Nearly 16% of the deliveries for the high variability restaurant exceed 30 minutes. On the other hand, only 2% of the deliveries take too long with the low variability restaurant. They both have an average delivery time of 20 minutes, but I know where I'd place my order when I'm hungry!

As this example shows, the central tendency doesn't provide complete information. We also need to understand the variability around the middle of the distribution to get the full picture. Now, let's move on to the different ways of measuring variability!

Range

Let's start with the range because it is the most straightforward measure of variability to calculate and the simplest to understand. The range of a dataset is the difference between the largest and smallest values in that dataset.

For example, in the two datasets below, dataset 1 has a range of 20 – 38 = 18 while dataset 2 has a range of 11 – 52 = 41. Dataset 2 has a broader range and, hence, more variability than dataset 1.

Dataset 1	Dataset 2
20	11
21	16
22	19
25	23
26	25
29	32
33	39
34	46
38	52

While ranges are easy to understand, they are based on only the two most extreme values in the dataset, which makes them very susceptible to outliers. If one of those numbers is unusually high or low, it affects the entire range even if it is atypical.

Additionally, the size of the dataset affects the range. In general, you are less likely to observe extreme values. However, as you increase the sample size, you have more opportunities to obtain extreme values. Consequently, when you draw random samples from the same population, the range tends to increase as the sample size increases. Accordingly, use the range to compare variability only when the sample sizes are similar.

The Interquartile Range (IQR) . . . and other Percentiles

As you learned before, the interquartile range is the middle half of the data. To visualize it, think about the median value that splits the dataset in half. Similarly, you can divide the data into quarters. Statisticians refer to these quarters as quartiles and denote them from low to high as Q1, Q2, Q3, and Q4. The lower quartile (Q1) is the highest value in the bottom quarter of the dataset. The upper quartile (Q3) splits the top quarter of the dataset from the lower three quarters. Q4 is the maximum value in the dataset.

The interquartile range is the middle half of the data that is in between the upper and lower quartiles. It's the 50% of data points that fall between Q1 and Q3. The IQR is the shaded area in the graph below.

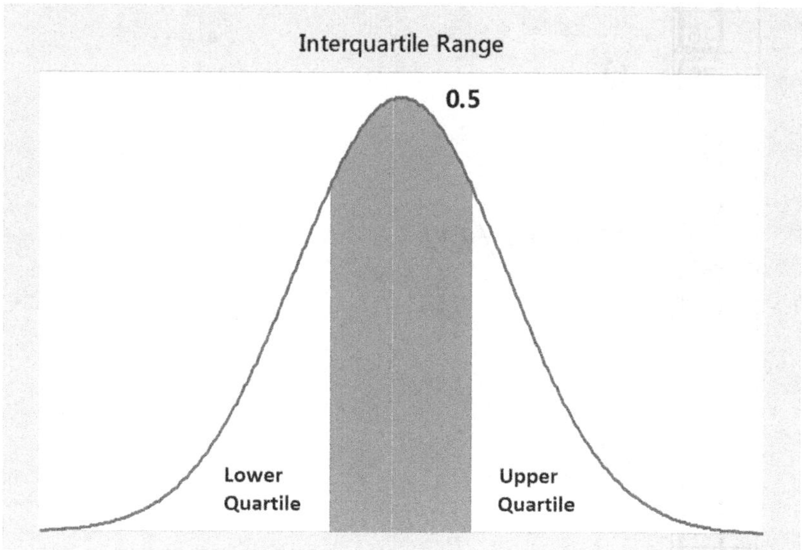

The broader the IQR, the higher the variability in your dataset. Additionally, the interquartile range is a robust measure of variability like the median is a robust measure of central tendency. Outliers don't dramatically influence either measure because neither depends on every value.

Additionally, the interquartile range is excellent for skewed distributions, just like the median. As you'll learn, when you have a normal distribution, the standard deviation tells you the percentage of observations that fall specific distances from the mean. However, this doesn't work for skewed distributions, and the IQR is an excellent alternative.

I've divided the dataset below by quartiles. The interquartile range extends from Q1 – Q3. For this dataset, the IQR is 20 – 39.

IQR	
58	Q4
55	
52	
46	
39	Q3
38	
34	
33	
29	Median / Q2
26	
25	
22	
21	
20	Q1
19	
16	
11	

Using other percentiles

When you have a skewed distribution, I find that reporting the median with the interquartile range is a particularly good combination. The interquartile range is equivalent to the region between the 75th and 25th percentile (75 – 25 = 50% of the data). You can also use other percentiles to determine the spread of different proportions. For example, the range between the 97.5th percentile and the 2.5th percentile covers 95% of the data.

Variance

Variance is the average squared difference of the values from the mean. Unlike the previous measures of variability, variance includes all values in the calculation by comparing each value to the mean. To calculate this statistic, you calculate a set of squared differences between the data points and the mean, sum them, and then divide by the number of observations. Hence, it's the average squared difference.

There are two formulas for variance depending on whether you are calculating variance for an entire population or using a sample to estimate the population variance. The equations are below, and then I work through an example in a table to help bring it to life.

Population variance

The formula for the variance of an entire population is the following:

$$\sigma^2 = \frac{\Sigma(X - \mu)^2}{N}$$

In the equation, σ^2 is the population parameter for the variance, μ is the parameter for the population mean, and N is the number of data points, which should include the entire population.

Sample variance

To use a sample to estimate the variance for a population, use the following formula. Using the previous equation with sample data tends to underestimate the variability. Because it's usually impossible to measure an entire population, statisticians use the equation for sample variances much more frequently.

$$s^2 = \frac{\Sigma(X - M)^2}{N - 1}$$

In the equation, s^2 is the sample variance, and M is the sample mean. N-1 in the denominator corrects for the tendency of a sample to underestimate the population variance.

Example of calculating the sample variance

I'll work through an example using the sample variance formula on a dataset with 17 observations in the table on the next page. The numbers in parentheses represent the corresponding table column number.

The procedure takes each observation (1), subtracts the sample mean (2) to calculate the difference (3), and squares that difference (4).

Then, the variance calculation sums the squared differences at the bottom of the table. Finally, it divides the sum and by 16 because we are calculating the sample variance equation for 17 observations (17 – 1 = 16). The variance for this dataset is 201.

The table on the next page works through these calculations.

1	2	3	4
Data Point	**Mean**	**Difference**	**Squared Difference**
11	32	-21	441
16	32	-16	256
19	32	-13	169
20	32	-12	144
21	32	-11	121
22	32	-10	100
25	32	-7	49
26	32	-6	36
29	32	-3	9
33	32	1	1
34	32	2	4
38	32	6	36
39	32	7	49
46	32	14	196
52	32	20	400
55	32	23	529
58	32	26	676

Sum	3216
Divide by 16	201
	Variance

Because the calculations use the squared differences, the variance is in squared units rather the original units of the data. While higher values of the variance indicate greater variability, there is no intuitive interpretation for specific values. Despite this limitation, various statistical tests use the variance in their calculations.

While it is difficult to interpret the variance itself, the standard deviation resolves this problem!

Standard Deviation

The standard deviation is the standard or typical difference between each data point and the mean. When the values in a dataset are grouped close together, you have a smaller standard deviation. Conversely, when the values are spread out more, the standard deviation increases because the typical distance between the datapoints and the mean grows.

Conveniently, the standard deviation uses the original units of the data, which makes interpretation easier. Consequently, the standard deviation is the most widely used measure of variability. For example, in the pizza delivery example, a standard deviation of 5 indicates that the typical delivery time is plus or minus 5 minutes from the mean. It's often reported along with the mean: 20 minutes (s.d. 5).

The standard deviation is just the square root of the variance. Recall that the variance is in squared units. Hence, the square root returns the value to the natural units. The symbol for the standard deviation as a population parameter is σ while s represents it as a sample estimate. To calculate the standard deviation, calculate the variance as shown in the previous section, and then take the square root of it. Voila! You have the standard deviation!

In the variance section, we calculated a variance of 201 in the table.

$$\sqrt{201} = 14.177$$

Therefore, the standard deviation for that dataset is 14.177.

When you have normally distributed data, or approximately so, the standard deviation becomes particularly valuable. You can use it to determine the proportion of the values that fall within a specified number of standard deviations from the mean. In chapter 4, I describe the Empirical Rule, which is how statisticians refer to this property, in the section about the Normal distribution.

Which One to Use?

First off, I'm crossing variance off the list because it is in squared units and doesn't provide an intuitive interpretation. Let's consider the others.

When you are comparing samples that are the same size, consider using the range as the measure of variability. It's a reasonably intuitive statistic. Just be aware that a single outlier can throw the range off. The range is particularly suitable for very small samples that don't have enough data to calculate the other measures reliably. Furthermore, the likelihood of obtaining an outlier is also lower for small samples.

When you have a skewed distribution, the median is a better measure of central tendency. Because the median is the 50th percentile, it makes sense to pair it with either the interquartile range or other percentile-based range.

For normally distributed data, or even data that aren't terribly skewed, using the tried and true combination reporting the mean and the standard deviation is the way to go. This combination is by far the most common.

Comparing Summary Statistics between Groups

In chapter 2, you saw how to assess the relationship between a categorical variable and a continuous variable using a boxplot. We saw how the central tendency and variability differs between groups. For reference, see the following boxplot. Now, let's do the same analysis but using the numeric measures of the mean and standard deviation.

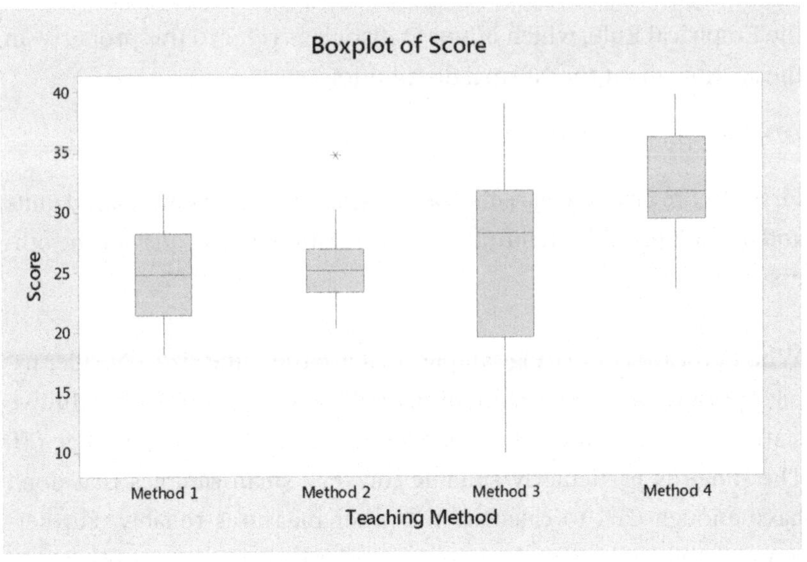

Now, let's calculate the mean and standard deviation for these groups.

Descriptive Statistics: Score

Variable	Teaching Method	Mean	StDev
Score	Method 1	24.792	3.849
	Method 2	25.269	3.136
	Method 3	26.070	7.510
	Method 4	32.221	4.376

When assessing the boxplot visually, we noticed the following similarities and differences. Method 1 and 2 have nearly identical medians, but Method 1 has somewhat more variability. Method 3 has the highest variability. Method 4 has the highest median.

The summary statistics reflect the boxplot findings, although the boxplot displays medians while we're calculating the mean. Method 4 has the highest mean. Method 3 has the highest standard deviation. Method 1 and 2 have nearly identical means and standard deviations. These values quantify the patterns in the graph.

Correlation

A correlation between variables indicates that as one variable changes in value, the other variable tends to change in a specific direction. Or, you can state it as a dependency. The value of one variable depends, to some degree, upon the value of another variable. Correlation measures the strength of that association.

Understanding that relationship is useful because we can use the value of one variable to predict the value of the other variable. For example, height and weight are correlated—as height increases, weight also tends to increase. Consequently, if we observe an unusually tall individual, we can predict that his weight is also above the average.

In statistics, correlation coefficients are a quantitative assessment that measures both the direction and the strength of this tendency to vary together. There are different types of correlation that you can use for different kinds of data. In this section, I cover the most common type of correlation—Pearson's correlation coefficient. Pearson's measures the strength of a linear relationship between a pair of continuous variables.

Before we get into the numbers, let's graph some data first so we can understand the concept behind what we are measuring.

As I showed in chapter 2, scatterplots are a great way to check for relationships between pairs of continuous data. The scatterplot displays the height and weight of pre-teenage girls you saw before. Each dot on the graph represents an individual girl and her combination of height and weight. These data are real values that I collected during an experiment.

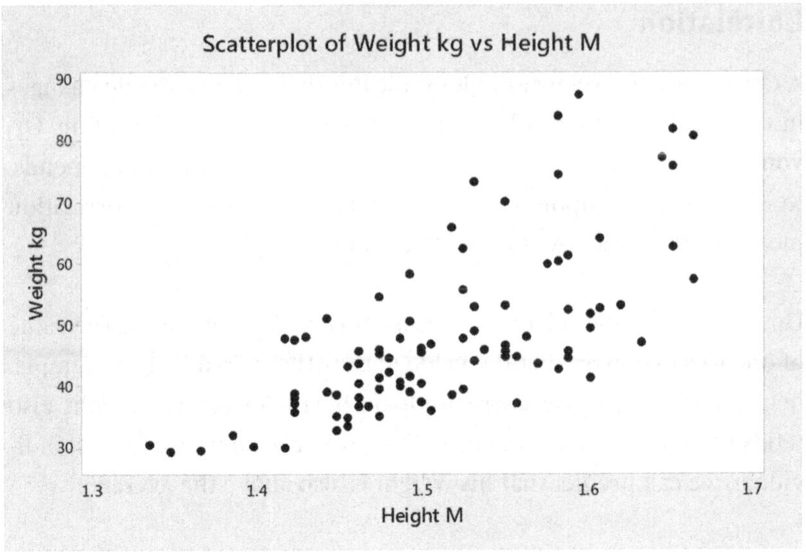

At a glance, you can see that there is a relationship between height and weight. As height increases, weight also tends to increase. However, it's not a perfect relationship. If you look at a specific height, say 1.5 meters, you can see that there is a range of weights associated with it. You can also find short people who weigh more than taller people. However, the general tendency that height and weight increase together is unquestionably present.

Pearson's correlation takes all of the data points on this graph and represents them as a single number. In this case, the statistical output below indicates that the Pearson's correlation coefficient is 0.694.

Correlation: Height M, Weight kg

```
Pearson correlation of Height M and Weight kg = 0.694
P-Value = 0.000
```

What does the correlation mean? We'll interpret the output soon. First, let's look at a range of possible correlation coefficients so we can understand how our height and weight example fits in.

Interpreting Correlation Coefficients

Pearson's correlation coefficient is represented by the Greek letter rho (ρ) for the population parameter and r for a sample statistic. This correlation coefficient is a single number that measures both the strength and direction of the linear relationship between two continuous variables. Values can range from -1 to +1.

- **Strength:** The greater the absolute value of the correlation coefficient, the stronger the relationship.
  - The extreme values of -1 and 1 indicate a perfectly linear relationship where a change in one variable is accompanied by a perfectly consistent change in the other. For these relationships, all of the data points fall on a line. In practice, you won't see either type of perfect relationship.
  - A coefficient of zero represents no linear relationship. As one variable increases, there is no tendency in the other variable to either increase or decrease.
  - When the value is in-between 0 and +1/-1, there is a relationship, but the points don't all fall on a line. As r approaches -1 or 1, the strength of the relationship increases, and the data points tend to fall closer to a line.

- **Direction:** The sign of the correlation coefficient represents the direction of the relationship.
  - Positive coefficients indicate that when the value of one variable increases, the value of the other variable also tends to increase. Positive relationships produce an upward slope on a scatterplot.
  - Negative coefficients represent indicate that when the value of one variable increases, the value of the other variable tends to decrease. Negative relationships produce a downward slope.

Examples of Positive and Negative Correlation Coefficients

A positive correlation exists between the speed of a wind turbine and the amount of energy it produces. As the turbine speed increases, electricity production also increases.

A negative correlation exists between outdoor temperature and heating costs. As the temperature increases, heating costs decrease.

Graphs for Different Correlation Coefficients

Charts always help bring concepts to life. The following scatterplots represent a spectrum of different correlation coefficients. I've held the horizontal and vertical scales of the scatterplots constant to allow for valid comparisons between them.

Correlation Coefficient = +1: A perfect positive relationship.

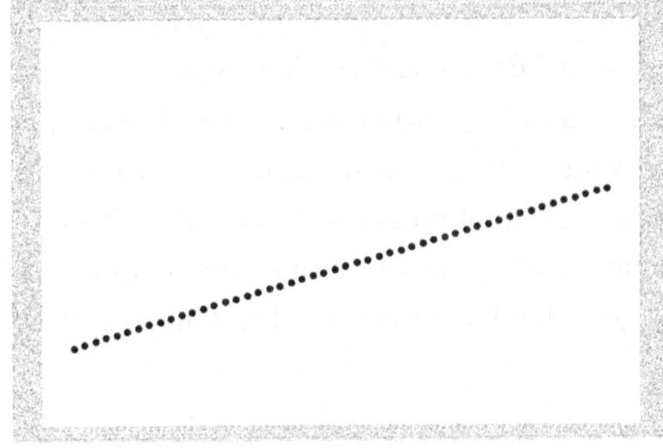

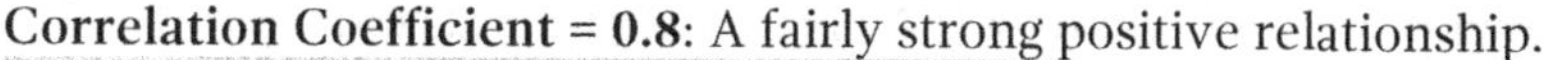

Correlation Coefficient = 0.8: A fairly strong positive relationship.

Correlation Coefficient = 0.6: A moderate positive relationship.

Correlation Coefficient = 0: No relationship. As one value increases, there is no tendency for the other value to change in a specific direction.

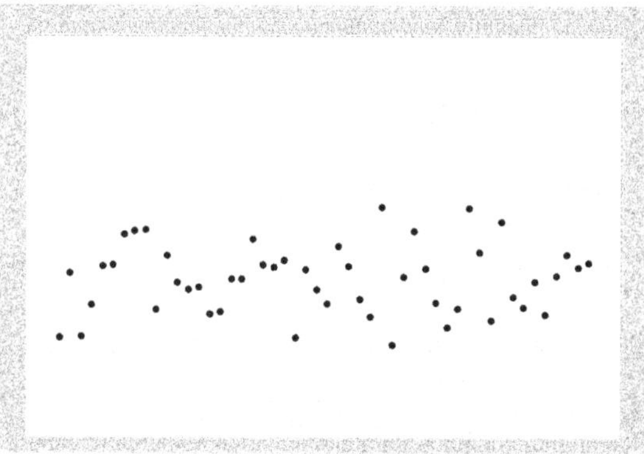

Correlation Coefficient = **-1**: A perfect negative relationship.

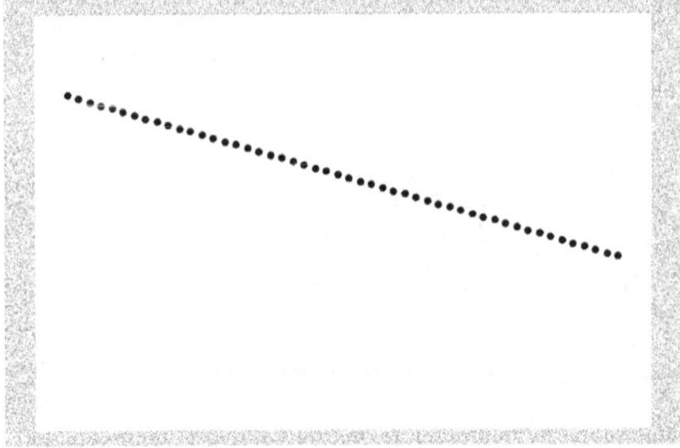

Correlation Coefficient = **-0.8**: A fairly strong negative relationship.

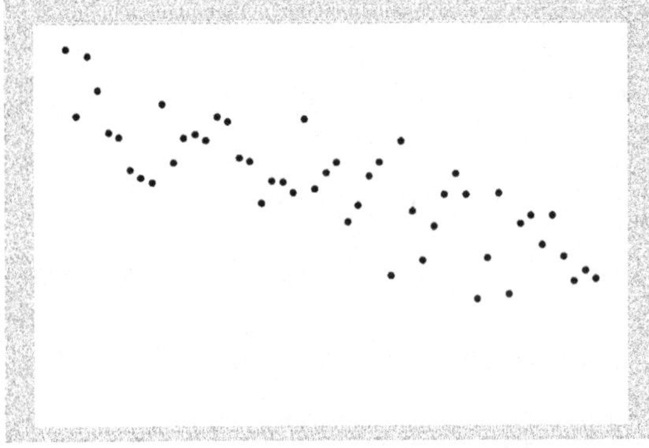

Correlation Coefficient = **-0.6**: A moderate negative relationship.

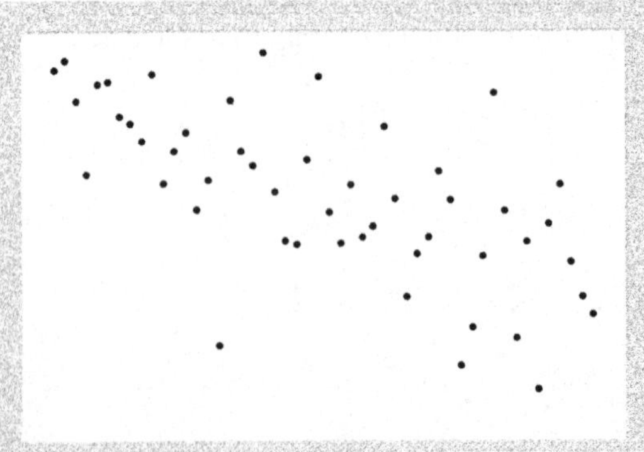

Discussion about the Scatterplots

For the scatterplots, I created one positive relationship between the variables and one negative relationship between the variables. Then, I varied only the amount of dispersion between the data points and the line that defines the relationship. That process illustrates how correlation measures the strength of the relationship. The stronger the association, the closer the data points fall to the line. I didn't include plots for weaker correlations that are closer to zero than 0.6 and -0.6 because they start to look like blobs of dots and it's hard to see the relationship.

A common misinterpretation is that negative correlation coefficients indicate there is no relationship. After all, a negative correlation sounds suspiciously like no relationship. However, the scatterplots for the negative correlations display real relationships. For negative correlation coefficients, high values of one variable are associated with low values of another variable. For example, there is a negative correlation between school absences and grades. As the number of absences increases, the grades decrease.

Earlier I mentioned how crucial it is to graph your data to understand them better. However, a quantitative measurement of the relationship does have an advantage. Graphs are a great way to visualize the data, but the scaling can exaggerate or weaken the appearance of a relationship. Additionally, the automatic scaling in most statistical software tends to make all data look similar.

Fortunately, Pearson's correlation coefficients are unaffected by scaling issues. Consequently, a statistical assessment is better for determining the precise strength of the relationship.

Graphs and the relevant statistical measures often work better in tandem.

Interpreting our Height and Weight Correlation Example

Now that we have seen a range of positive and negative relationships, let's see how our correlation coefficient of 0.694 fits in. We know that it's a positive relationship. As height increases, weight tends to increase. Regarding the strength of the relationship, the graph shows that it's not a very strong relationship where the data points tightly hug a line. However, it's not an entirely amorphous blob with a very low correlation. It's somewhere in between. That description matches our moderate correlation coefficient of 0.694.

Pearson's Measures Linear Relationship

Pearson's correlation coefficients measure only *linear* relationships. Consequently, if your data contain a curvilinear relationship, the correlation coefficient will not detect it. For example, the correlation for the data in the scatterplot below is zero. However, there is a relationship between the two variables—it's just not linear.

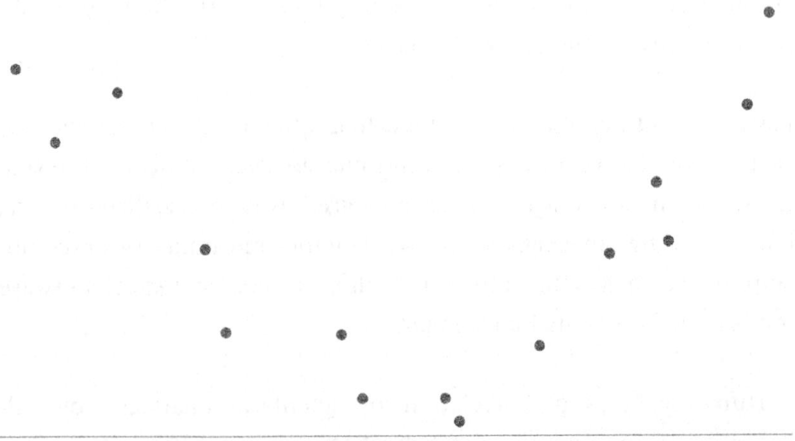

This example illustrates another reason to graph your data! Just because the coefficient is near zero, it doesn't necessarily indicate there is no relationship.

Correlation Does Not Imply Causation

I'm sure you've heard this expression before, and it is a crucial warning. Correlation between two variables indicates that changes in one variable are associated with changes in the other variable. However, correlation does not mean that changes in one variable actually *cause* changes in the other variable.

Sometimes a relationship is obviously causal. For the height and weight data, it makes sense that adding more vertical structure to a body *causes* the total mass to increase. Or, increasing the wattage of lightbulbs *causes* the light output to increase.

However, in other cases, a causal relationship does not exist. Instead, it's merely an association. As the value of variable A increases, the value of variable B also increases. However, if it is correlation but not causation, then the changes in variable A are not causing the changes in variable B.

How does it come to be that variables are correlated but do not have a causal relationship? A common reason is a spurious correlation. A spurious correlation is a situation where two variables appear to have an association, but in reality, a third factor causes that association. That third factor is known as a confounding variable. A confounding variable correlates with both of your variables of interest and can create confusion about which relationships are causal and which are merely spurious associations. In a study, the confounding variable might be the real causal factor!

For example, ice cream sales and shark attacks have a positive correlation. Clearly, selling more ice cream does not cause shark attacks (or vice versa).

In this example, the number of people at the beach is a confounding variable. Again, a confounding variable correlates with both variables of interest—ice cream and shark attacks in our example.

In the diagram below, imagine that as the number of people increases, ice cream sales also tend to increase. In turn, more people at the beach cause shark attacks to increase because the sharks have more opportunities. The correlation structure creates an apparent, or spurious, correlation between ice cream sales and shark attacks, but it isn't causation.

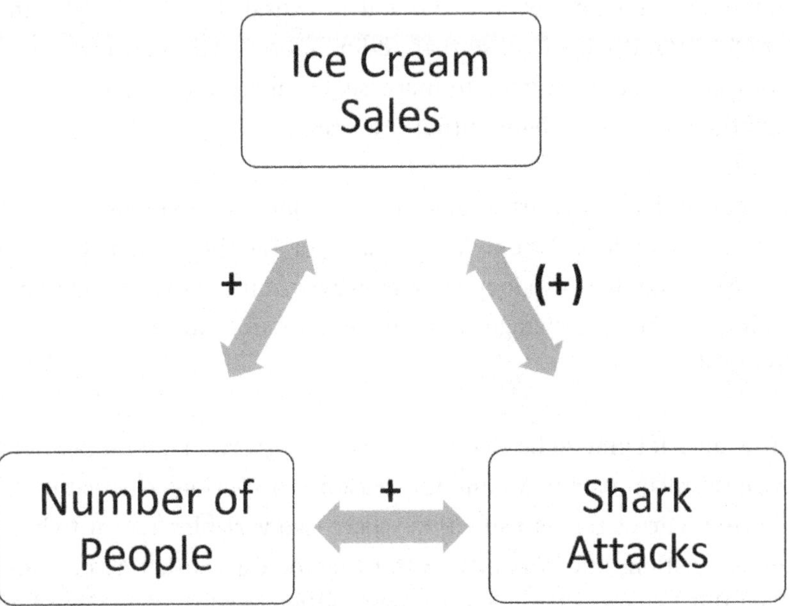

Confounders are a common reason for non-causal associations between variables. In statistics, you typically need to perform a randomized, controlled experiment to determine that a relationship is causal rather than merely correlation—which we'll cover in chapter 7.

How Strong of a Correlation is Considered Good?

What is a good correlation? How high should it be? I am frequently asked these questions. I have seen several schemes that attempt to classify correlations as strong, medium, and weak.

However, there is only one correct answer. The correlation coefficient should accurately reflect the strength of the relationship. Take a look at the correlation between the height and weight data, 0.694. It's not a very strong relationship, but it accurately represents our data. Accurate representations are the best-case scenario for using a statistic to describe an entire dataset.

The strength of any relationship naturally depends on the specific pair of variables. Some research questions involve weaker relationships than other subject areas. Case in point, humans are hard to predict. Studies that assess relationships involving human behavior tend to have correlation coefficients weaker than +/- 0.6.

However, if you analyze two variables in a physical process, and have very precise measurements, you might expect correlations near +1 or -1. There is no one-size-fits-all best answer for how strong a relationship should be. The correct correlation value depends on your study area.

Summary and Next Steps

In this chapter, we covered measures of central tendency, measures of variability, and correlation coefficients. They are summary statistics that describe a dataset using a single number. Importantly, you learned how the properties of your dataset play a role in determining which measures to use. Additionally, the chapter showed how these measures relate to, and complement, the graphs we've been using.

We also covered percentiles. Percentiles represent the relative standing of a value within a dataset or population. Percentiles are helpful when you need to know where a specific value falls within a distribution of values. Percentiles are especially flexible because you can also use them as measures of central tendency (median) and variability (IQR).

Up to this point, we've discussed the center and spread of distributions by using graphs and summary statistics to reveal these properties. The next chapter focuses on probability distributions, which are mathematical functions that describe distributions and calculate probabilities.

CHAPTER 4

Probability Distributions

In statistics, random variables are characteristics that you can observe, but you don't control them. They can be a characteristic, measurement, or a count that varies randomly according to a function. Random in this context indicates that you don't know the value of the next observation, but you do know the probability associated with values and ranges of values.

A probability distribution is a mathematical function that describes the probabilities for all possible outcomes of a random variable. In other words, the frequency of the observed values varies based on the underlying probability distribution.

These technical descriptions make the concept sound more complicated than it actually is. Just imagine any characteristic that you measure for an experiment, a study, or just something in which you're interested. The values for this characteristic that you observe will vary based on underlying probabilities. Probability distributions display the probabilities for all possible values.

Suppose you draw a random sample and measure the heights of the subjects. As you measure heights, you'll notice that some heights are more common while others are rare. Probability distributions are useful when you need to know which outcomes are most likely, the spread of potential values, and the likelihood of different results. What is the probability that the next height measurement will be taller than two meters?

We've discussed the properties of distributions in histograms, and probability distributions are similar. They have a shape, center, and spread. However, the focus for probability distributions is, unsurprisingly, on the probabilities of the outcomes. Importantly, probability distributions describe populations while histograms represent samples.

In this chapter, you'll learn about probability distributions for both discrete and continuous variables. I'll show you how they work and examples of how to use them. But first, some notation and rules.

Probability distributions indicate the likelihood of an event or outcome. Statisticians use the following notation to describe probabilities:

p(x) = the likelihood that random variable takes a specific value of x.

The sum of all probabilities for all possible values must equal 1. Furthermore, the probability for a particular value or range of values must be between 0 and 1, inclusive.

Probability distributions describe the dispersion of the values for a random variable. Consequently, the kind of variable determines the type of probability distribution. For a single random variable, statisticians divide distributions into the following two types:

- Discrete probability distributions for discrete variables
- Probability density functions for continuous variables

You can use equations and tables of variable values and probabilities to represent a probability distribution. However, I prefer to graph them using probability distribution plots. As you'll notice in the examples that follow, the differences between discrete and continuous probability distributions are immediately apparent. You'll see why I love these graphs!

Discrete Probability Distributions

Discrete probability functions are also known as probability mass functions and can assume a set of distinct values. For example, coin tosses and counts of events are discrete functions. These are discrete distributions because there are no in-between values. For example, you can have only heads or tails in a coin toss. Similarly, if you're counting the number of books that a library checks out per hour, you can count 21 or 22 books, but nothing in between.

For discrete probability distribution functions, each possible value has a non-zero likelihood. Furthermore, the probabilities for all possible values must sum to one. Because the total probability is 1, one of the values must occur for each opportunity.

For example, the likelihood of rolling a specific number on a die is 1/6. The total probability for all six values equals one. When you throw a die, you inevitably obtain one of the possible values.

If the discrete distribution has a finite number of values, you can display all the values with their corresponding probabilities in a table. For example, according to a study, the likelihood of the number of cars in a California household is the following:

Number of Cars	Probability
0	0.03
1	0.13
2	0.70
3	0.10
4+	0.04

Types of Discrete Distribution

There are a variety of discrete probability distributions that you can use to model different types of data. The correct discrete distribution depends on the properties of your data. For example, use the:

- Binomial distribution to model binary data, such as coin tosses.
- Poisson distribution to model count data, such as the count of library book checkouts per hour.
- Uniform distribution to model multiple events with the same probability, such as rolling a die.

Analysts use discrete distributions for binary data most frequently. Consequently, they'll be my focus in this chapter.

Binomial and Other Distributions for Binary Data

Binary data occur when you can place an observation into only two categories. It tells you that an event occurred or that an item has a particular characteristic. For instance, an inspection process produces binary pass/fail results. Or, when a customer enters a store, there are two possible outcomes—sale or no sale. In a flu vaccination study, the binary outcomes for the human subjects are either "infected" or "not infected" with the flu.

At a basic level, binary data allow you to calculate proportions and percentages easily. What is the proportion of items that pass the inspection? What percentage of customers make a purchase?

In this section, I show you how to use the binomial, geometric, negative binomial, and the hypergeometric distributions to glean more information from your binary data. Use these distributions to model probabilities and the frequency of occurrences. For example:

- How many times is an event likely to occur?
- When is the first instance probable?
- How many opportunities do I need to produce a specific number of events?

Being able to answer these questions can be quite valuable. How do you provide these answers? All you need are several convenient, discrete probability distributions designed for binary data. I'll show you the benefits of using the binomial, geometric, negative binomial, and hypergeometric distributions. Each of these distributions allows you to answer different questions about your binary data.

Assumptions for Using Probability Distributions for Binary Data

To use the binomial, geometric, negative binomial, and the hypergeometric distributions, you need to satisfy the following assumptions.

1. **There are only two possible outcomes per trial**. For example, accept or reject, sale or no sale, etc.
2. **Each trial is independent (except for hypergeometric)**. The result of one trial does not affect the results of another trial. For instance, when flipping a coin, the outcome of a coin toss doesn't influence the next coin toss.
3. **The probability remains constant over time (except for hypergeometric)**. In some cases, this assumption is valid based on the physical properties, such as flipping a coin. However, if there is a chance the probability can change over time, you can use the P chart (a control chart) to confirm this assumption. For example, the likelihood that a process produces defective products might change over time.

Throughout most of these distributions, I'll use a die rolling example. Assume we're playing a game where rolling a 6 is very advantageous. In this scenario, rolling a 6 is binary because an observation can be either a 6 or not a 6. The probability of rolling a 6 is 1/6, or about

0.1667. We'll use the binomial, geometric, and negative binomial distributions to calculate probabilities for how many 6s we'll roll, when they'll first appear, and the likelihood of observing a certain number of 6s.

In the examples, I'll show you when to use each distribution and how to interpret the results. I'll cover both how to understand the probability for a specific outcome and the cumulative probability for a range of outcomes. Consequently, it's essential to notice differences between the probabilities for discrete values (each bar in the graphs) and cumulative probabilities that sum probabilities for all bars in a shaded region.

Binomial Distribution

Use the binomial distribution to calculate probabilities that an event occurs a certain number of times in a set number of trials. Specifically, it calculates the probability of X events happening within N trials.

Suppose you want to determine how likely it is to roll 6s on a die when you roll it ten times. Additionally, let's learn the cumulative probability of rolling 6s four or more times.

I'll use statistical software to graph the results using the binomial distribution and enter a probability of 0.1667 and specify ten trials.

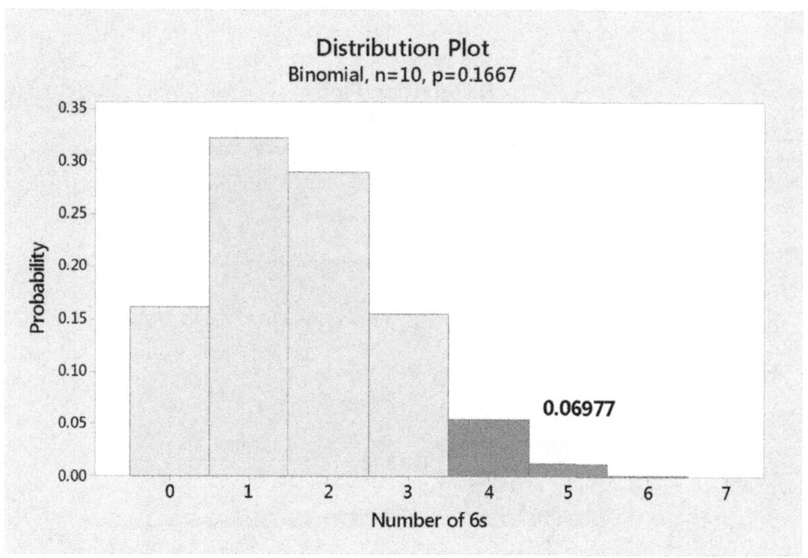

The graph displays the probability of rolling a 6 each number of times when you roll the die ten times. For example, the highest probability (0.32) occurs with rolling a 6 precisely one time in ten rolls. We have a 16% chance of rolling no 6s. We also want to determine the probability of rolling 6s four or more times. The shaded area sums the probabilities for four events and higher to calculate this cumulative probability. The cumulative probability of rolling at least four 6s is 0.06977.

Geometric Distribution

Use the geometric distribution when you know the probability of an event occurring and want to calculate the likelihood of the event first occurring during a specific trial. In other words, if you keep drawing random samples, what is the probability of the event/characteristic first appearing on each draw?

With the die example, we'll use the geometric distribution to determine the probability of rolling the first 6 on different numbers of rolls. Additionally, we want to learn the cumulative probability that the first 6 appears on the 7th roll or later.

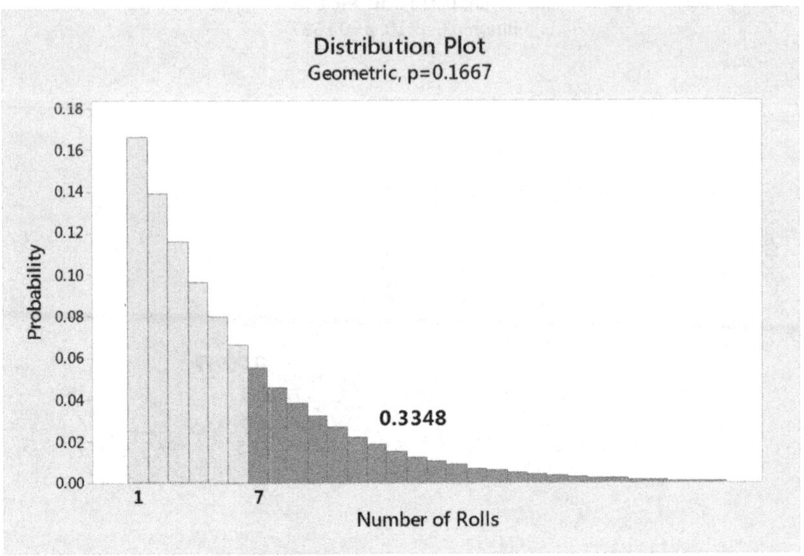

Each bar in the graph represents the probability of rolling the first six on a specific trial. For instance, the likelihood of rolling the first 6 on the third roll specifically is 0.11. Interestingly, you might think you're virtually guaranteed to get a 6 when you roll the die six times. However, the shaded region indicates that you have a 33% cumulative chance of rolling the first 6 on the 7th roll or later.

Negative Binomial Distribution

Use the negative binomial distribution to calculate the number of trials that are required to observe the event a specific number of times. In other words, given a known probability of an event occurring and the number of events that you specify, this distribution calculates the probability for observing that number of events within N trials.

For the die example, suppose we want to determine the probability of rolling 6s five times based on the number of total rolls. Additionally, we want to assess the cumulative probability to determine the number of rolls necessary to have a 50% chance of rolling five 6s.

In the statistical software, I enter the probability and specify 5 events.

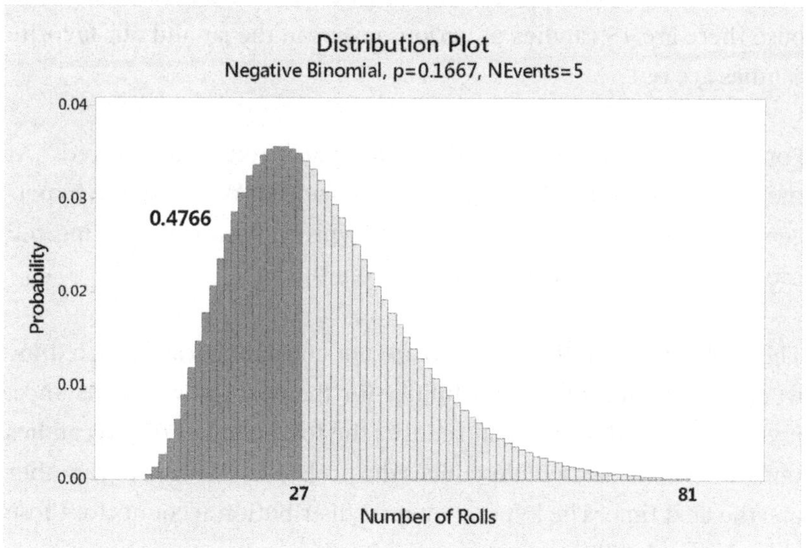

In the plot, each bar represents the probability of rolling precisely five 6s in the specified number of rolls. For example, the maximum likelihood (0.04) of rolling exactly five 6s occurs at 24 rolls, which is the peak of the histogram. Additionally, the shaded area indicates that the cumulative probability of obtaining five 6s in the first 27 rolls is nearly 0.5.

Hypergeometric Distribution

Use the hypergeometric distribution when you are drawing from a small population without replacement, and you want to calculate probabilities that an event occurs a certain number of times in a set amount of trials. Like the binomial distribution, the hypergeometric distribution calculates the probability of X events in N trials. However, unlike the binomial distribution, it does not assume that the likelihood of an event's occurrence is constant. Instead, the hypergeometric distribution assumes that the probability changes because you are drawing from a small population without replacement.

To illustrate how to use this distribution, we have to move away from rolling 6s on our die. Instead, we'll draw candy blindly from a jar. Suppose there are 15 candies of various colors in the jar and our favorite candies are red.

For this scenario, the binary data values are "red" and "not red." At the start, 5 out of the 15 (33%) candies are red. We'll use the hypergeometric distribution to calculate the probabilities of drawing red candies when we draw five candies from the jar.

The probabilities in this scenario are not constant because each draw from the jar affects the probabilities for the next draw. For instance, if you draw a red candy, that reduces the total number of red candies remaining in the jar, which reduces the probability of drawing another one the next time. The hypergeometric distribution accounts for these changing probabilities.

In the statistical software, I specify the following:

- The population size is 15.
- There are five red candies.
- We'll draw 5 candies from the jar randomly.

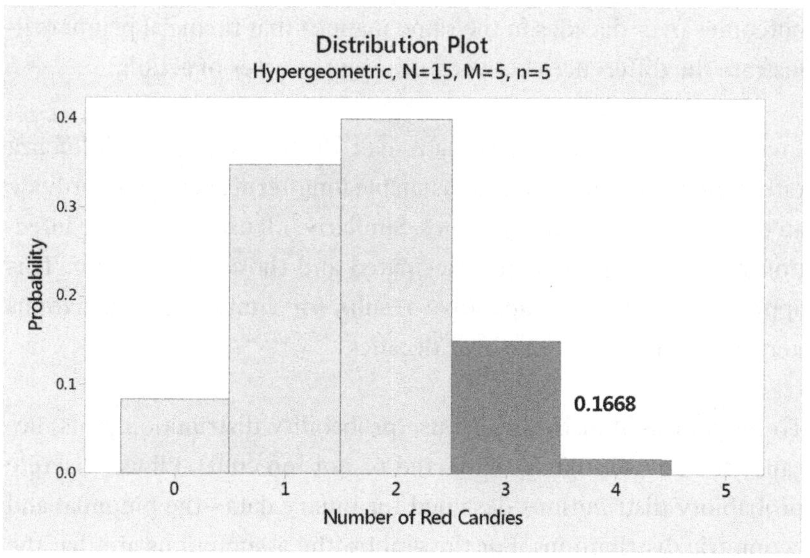

The graph displays the probability of drawing each possible number of red candies when you draw 5 candies altogether. For example, the highest probability is approximately 0.4 and occurs with obtaining two red candies. There is an 8% chance of getting no red candies. And, you have a cumulative probability of 0.1668 for drawing at least three red candies. More likely than not, you'll have to be content with 1 or 2 red candies!

The binomial, geometric, negative binomial, and hypergeometric distributions describe the probabilities associated with the number of events and when they occur. This information can be invaluable for planning purposes. I kept the die and candy examples intentionally simple so they are easy to understand. However, for a science-based, real-world example, read about the effectiveness of flu shots in the next section.

Modelling Flu Outcomes Over Decades

Flu shots benefits are like investing year-after-year. The cumulative effect magnifies the differences over time. I'm going to model flu outcomes over decades in the same manner that financial planners illustrate the differences between different courses of action.

Investment return rates fluctuate over the years, just like influenza rates. Financial planners use reasonable long-term averages to provide an estimate of different outcomes. Similarly, I'll use the average infection rate for those who are vaccinated and those who are not. This approach produces comparative results for annual flu vaccinations versus no flu vaccinations over decades.

To model this statistically, I'll use probability distribution plots. Because the data are binary (infected or not infected), I'll use discrete probability distributions designed for binary data—the binomial and geometric distributions. For the graphs, the assumptions are that the average infection rate for the:

- Unvaccinated is 7.0% annually.
- Vaccinated is 1.9% annually.

I based these average infection rates on multiple randomized controlled studies of flu shots. See the references at the end of the book for a listing.

We'll learn what effect that 5.1% difference has over decades. I'll compare two different scenarios—getting the flu shot every year versus never getting the influenza vaccination. Using our estimates, I'll answer two questions:

- How long until my first case of the flu on average?
- How many times will I get the flu?

In both plots, the left panel displays the no flu shot scenario while the right panel shows the annual influenza vaccine scenario.

How long until my first case of the flu on average?

I'll use the geometric distribution to model the probability of first catching the flu. Each bar in the graph indicates the likelihood of first getting the flu in a specific year. The risk for any given year is small. More importantly, I've shaded the graphs to indicate the number of years until the cumulative probability reaches 50%. The chart stops at 65 years because flu shot effectiveness decreases around that age.

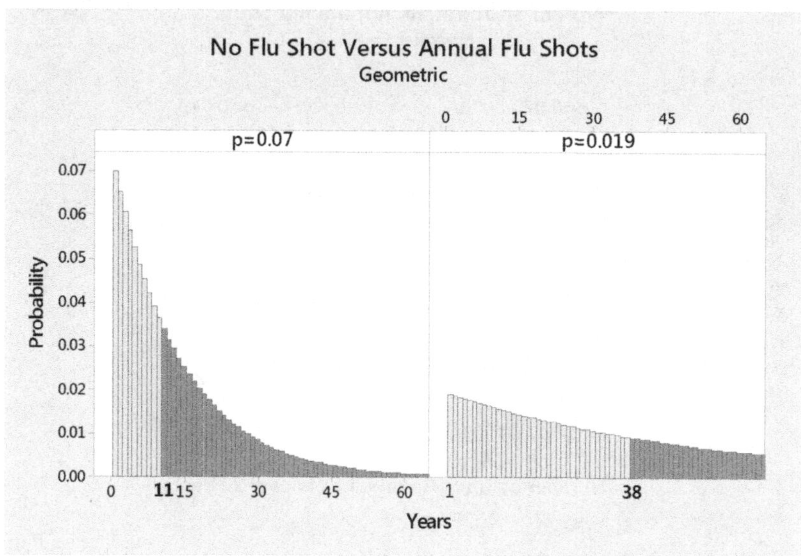

The chart shows how your probability of first contracting the flu is much higher early on when you aren't vaccinated (left) than when you are regularly vaccinated.

The left panel indicates that without flu shots, you have a 50/50 chance of getting the flu in 11 years. On the other hand, the right panel displays the probabilities for when you are vaccinated annually. You don't reach a 50% cumulative probability until 38 years. Furthermore, when you never get the flu shot, you have only a 6.8% chance of not catching the flu in 38 years (not shown)!

How often will I catch the flu?

Let's statistically model the number of times you can expect to catch the flu in 20 years. For this graph, I'll use the binomial distribution. Each bar indicates the likelihood of catching the flu the specified number of times. I've shaded the bars to represent the cumulative probability of catching the flu at least twice in 20 years.

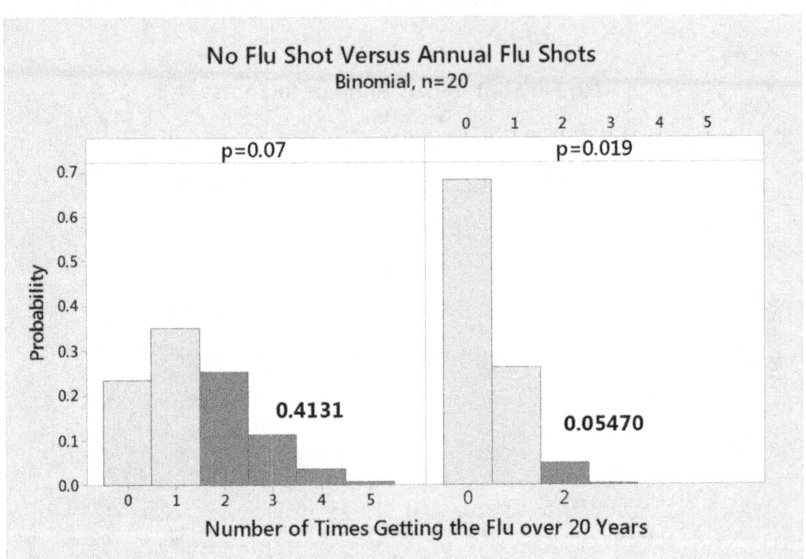

A significant difference jumps out at you—which demonstrates the power of probability distribution plots! The tallest bar on the graph is the one in the right panel that represents zero cases of the flu in 20 years when you get flu shots. When you vaccinate annually, you have a 68% chance of not catching the flu within 20 years! Conversely, if you don't vaccinate, you have only a 23% of escaping the flu entirely.

In the left panel, the distribution spreads out much further than in the right panel. Without vaccinations, you have a 41% chance of getting the flu at least twice in 20 years compared to 5% with annual vaccinations. Some unlucky unvaccinated folks will get the flu four or five times during that period!

Now, let's switch gears and move on to continuous data!

Continuous Probability Distributions

Continuous probability functions are also known as probability density functions. You know that you have a continuous distribution if the variable can assume an infinite number of values between any two values. Continuous variables are often measurements on a scale, such as height, weight, and temperature.

Unlike discrete probability distributions where each particular value has a non-zero likelihood, specific values in continuous distributions have a zero probability. For example, the likelihood of measuring a temperature that is exactly 32 degrees is zero.

Why? Consider that the current temperature can be an infinite number of other temperatures that are infinitesimally higher or lower than 32. Statisticians say that an individual value has an infinitesimally small probability that is equivalent to zero.

How to Find Probabilities for Continuous Data

Probabilities for continuous distributions are calculated for ranges of values rather than single points. A probability indicates the likelihood that a value will fall within an interval. This property is simple to demonstrate using a probability distribution plot—which we'll get to soon!

On a probability plot, the entire area under the distribution curve equals 1. This fact is equivalent to how the sum of all probabilities must equal one for discrete distributions. The proportion of the area under a curve that falls within a range of values along the X-axis represents the likelihood a value will fall within that range. Finally, you can't have an area under the curve with only a single value, which explains why the probability equals zero for an individual value.

Characteristics of Continuous Probability Distributions

Just as there are different types of discrete distributions for different kinds of discrete data, there are different distributions for continuous data. Each probability distribution has parameters that define its shape. Most distributions have between 1-3 parameters. Specifying these parameters establishes the shape of the distribution and all of its probabilities entirely. These parameters represent essential properties of the distribution, such as the central tendency and the variability.

The most well-known continuous distribution is the normal distribution, which is also known as the Gaussian distribution or the "bell curve." This symmetric distribution fits a wide variety of phenomena, such as human height and IQ scores. It has two parameters—the mean and the standard deviation. The Weibull distribution and the lognormal distribution are other common continuous distributions. Both of these distributions can fit skewed data.

Distribution parameters are values that apply to entire populations. Unfortunately, population parameters are generally unknown because it's usually impossible to measure an entire population. However, you can use random samples to calculate estimates of these parameters and use them with probability distributions.

To determine which distribution provides the best fit for your sample data, you'll need to perform hypothesis tests and use special graphs. Learn more about this process in my ebook about hypothesis testing.

Example of Using the Normal Probability Distribution

Let's start with the normal distribution to show how to use continuous probability distributions.

The distribution of IQ scores is defined as a normal distribution with a mean of 100 and a standard deviation of 15. We'll create the probability plot of this distribution. Additionally, let's determine the likelihood that an IQ score will be between 120-140.

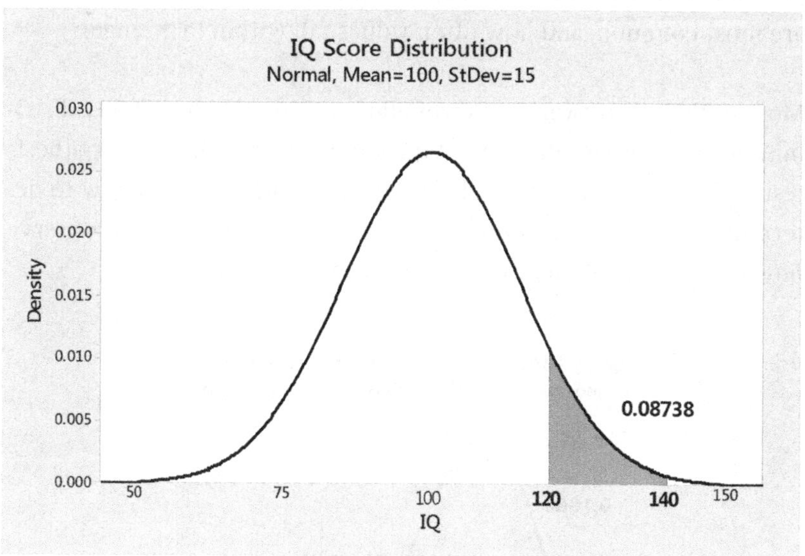

Examine the properties of the probability plot above. We can see that it is a symmetric distribution where values occur most frequently around 100, which is the mean. The probabilities drop-off equally as you move away from the mean in both directions. The shaded area for the range of IQ scores between 120-140 contains 8.738% of the total area under the curve. Therefore, the likelihood that an IQ score falls within this range is 0.08738.

Example of Using the Lognormal Probability Distribution

As I mentioned, I really like probability distribution plots because they make distribution properties crystal clear. In the case above, we used the normal distribution. Because that distribution is so well-known, you might have guessed the general appearance of the chart. Now, let's look at a less intuitive example.

Suppose you are told that the body fat percentages for teenage girls follow a lognormal distribution with a location of 3.32317 and a scale of 0.24188. Furthermore, you're asked to determine the probability that body fat percentage values will fall between 20-24%. Huh? It's probably not clear what the shape of this distribution is, which values are most common, and how often values fall within that range!

Most statistical software packages allow you to plot probability distributions and answer all of these questions at once. In my hypothesis testing book, I include the relevant dataset and show you how to determine that this distribution provides the best fit. For now, observe how helpful probability distributions can be.

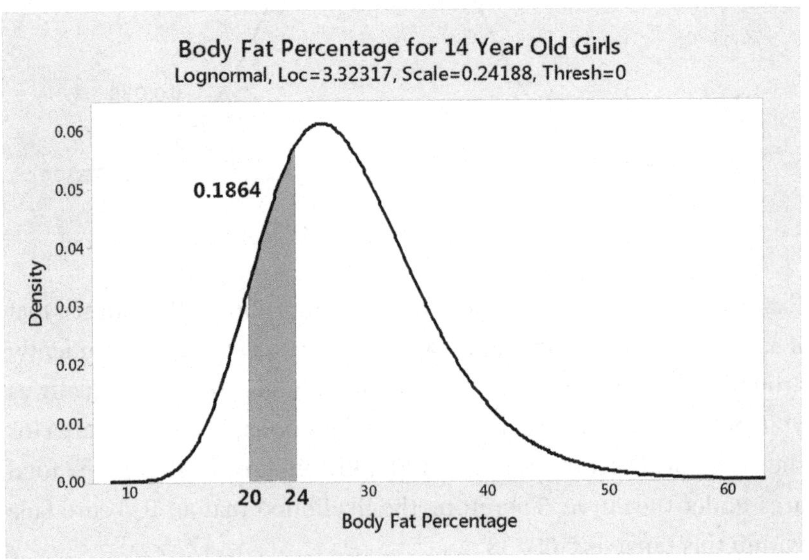

The graph displays both the shape of the distribution and how our range of interest fits within it. We can see that it is a right-skewed distribution, and the most common values fall near 26%. Furthermore, our range of interest falls below the curve's peak and contains 18.64% of the occurrences.

As you can see, these graphs are an effective way to report complex distribution information to a lay audience.

Normal Distribution in Depth

The normal distribution is the most important probability distribution in statistics because it fits many natural phenomena. For example, heights, blood pressure, measurement error, and IQ scores follow the normal distribution. It is also known as the Gaussian distribution and the bell curve.

The normal distribution is a probability function that describes how the values of a variable are distributed. It is a symmetric distribution where most of the observations cluster around the central peak and the probabilities for values further away from the mean taper off equally in both directions. Extreme values in both tails of the distribution are similarly unlikely.

In this section, you'll learn how to use the normal distribution, its parameters, and how to calculate Z-scores to standardize your data and find probabilities.

Height data are normally distributed. The distribution in this example fits real data that I collected from 14-year-old girls during a study.

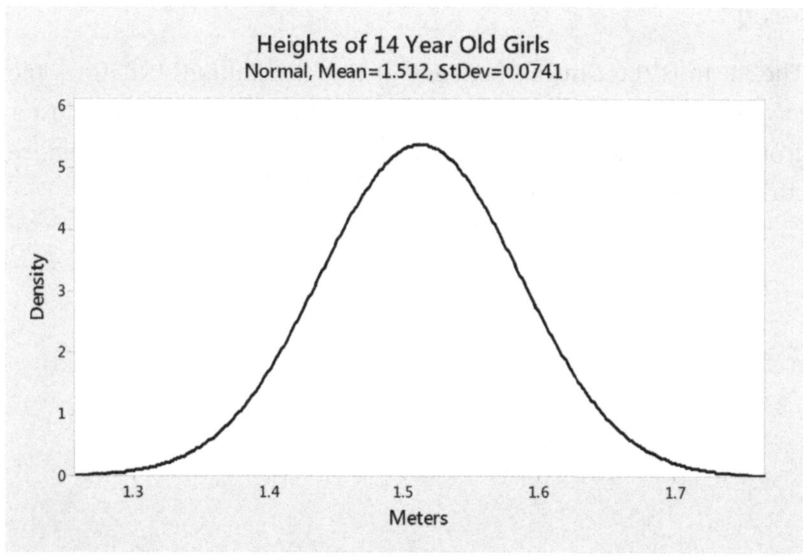

As you can see, the distribution of heights follows the typical pattern for all normal distributions. Most girls are close to the average (1.512 meters). Small differences between an individual's height and the mean occur more frequently than substantial deviations from the mean. The standard deviation is 0.0741m, which indicates the typical distance that individual girls tend to fall from mean height.

The distribution is symmetric. The number of girls shorter than average equals the number of girls taller than average. In both tails of the distribution, extremely short girls occur as infrequently as extremely tall girls.

Parameters of the Normal Distribution

As with any probability distribution, the parameters for the normal distribution define its shape and probabilities entirely. The normal distribution has two parameters, the mean and standard deviation. The normal distribution does not have just one form. Instead, the shape changes based on the parameter values, as shown in the following graphs.

Mean

The mean is the central tendency of the distribution. It defines the location of the peak for normal distributions. Most values cluster around the mean. On a graph, changing the mean shifts the entire curve left or right on the X-axis.

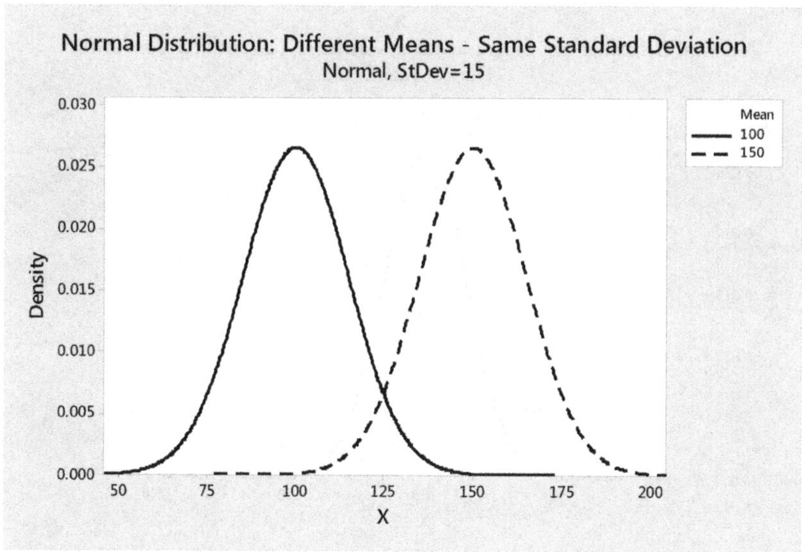

Standard deviation

The standard deviation is a measure of variability. It defines the width of the normal distribution. The standard deviation determines how far away from the mean the values tend to fall. It represents the typical distance between the observations and the average.

On a graph, changing the standard deviation either tightens or spreads out the width of the distribution along the X-axis. Larger standard deviations produce distributions that are more spread out.

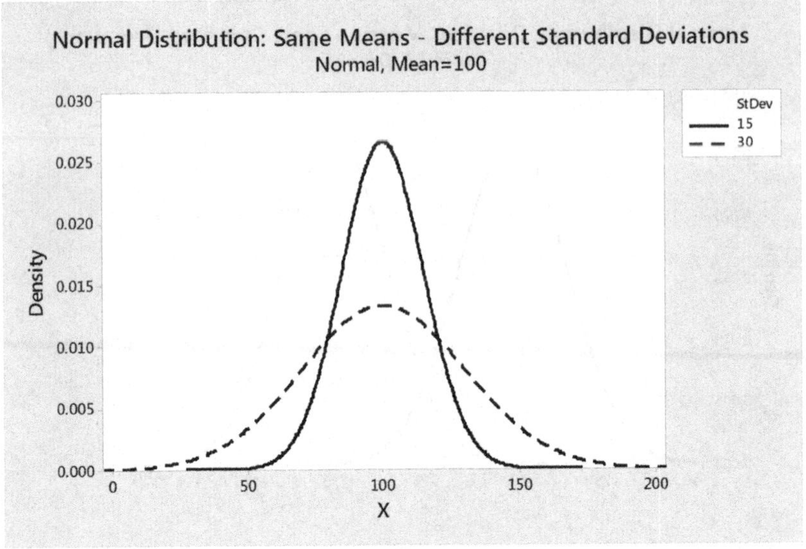

When you have narrow distributions, probabilities are higher that values won't fall far from the mean. As you increase the spread, the likelihood that observations will be further away from the mean also increases.

Population parameters versus sample estimates

The mean and standard deviation are parameter values that apply to entire populations. For the normal distribution, statisticians signify the parameters by using the Greek symbol μ (mu) for the population mean and σ (sigma) for the population standard deviation.

Unfortunately, population parameters are usually unknown because it's generally impossible to measure an entire population. However, you can use random samples to estimate these parameters. Statisticians represent parameter estimates using $\bar{x}$ for the sample mean and s for the sample standard deviation. The next chapter focuses on this process.

Properties of the Normal Distribution

Despite the different shapes, all forms of the normal distribution have the following characteristic properties.

- They're all symmetric. The normal distribution cannot model skewed distributions.
- The mean, median, and mode are all equal.
- Half of the population is less than the mean and half is greater than the mean.
- The Empirical Rule allows you to determine the proportion of values that fall within certain distances from the mean. More on this below!

While the normal distribution is essential in statistics, it is just one of many probability distributions, and it does not fit all data. The weights in the previous section came from the same individuals as the heights in this section. However, while their heights are normally distributed, their weights are not. Instead, the weights are right-skewed and follow the lognormal distribution.

The Empirical Rule

When you have normally distributed data, the standard deviation becomes particularly valuable. You can use the Empirical Rule to determine the proportion of values that fall within a specified number of standard deviations from the mean. For example, in a normal distribution, 68% of the observations fall within +/- 1 standard deviation from the mean.

Mean +/- standard deviations	Percentage of data contained
1	68%
2	95%
3	99.7%

Let's look at a pizza delivery example. Assume that a pizza restaurant has a mean delivery time of 30 minutes and a standard deviation of 5 minutes. Using the Empirical Rule, we can determine that 68% of the delivery times are between 25-35 minutes (30 +/- 5), 95% are between 20-40 minutes (30 +/- 2*5), and 99.7% are between 15-45 minutes (30 +/-3*5). The chart below illustrates this property graphically.

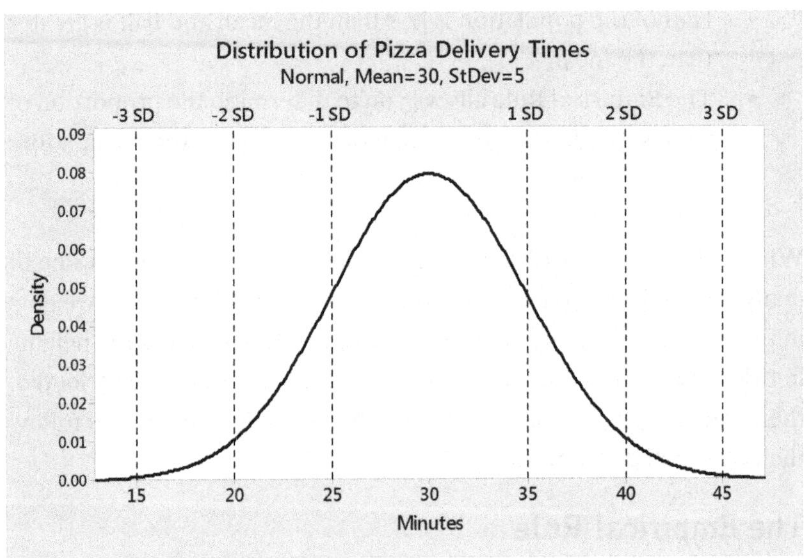

Standard Normal Distribution and Standard Scores

As you've seen, the normal distribution has many different shapes depending on the parameter values. However, the standard normal distribution is a special case of the normal distribution where the mean is zero and the standard deviation is 1. This distribution is also known as the Z-distribution.

A value on the standard normal distribution is known as a standard score or a Z-score. A standard score represents the number of standard deviations above or below the mean that a specific observation falls. For example, a standard score of 1.5 indicates that the observation is 1.5 standard deviations above the mean. On the other hand, a negative score represents a value below the average. The mean has a Z-score of 0.

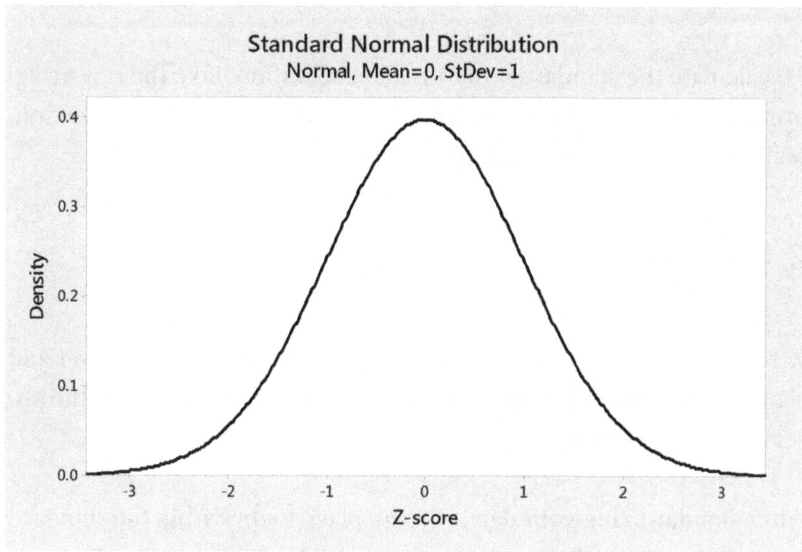

Suppose you weigh an apple and it weighs 110 grams. There's no way to tell from the weight alone how this apple compares to other apples. However, as you'll see, after you calculate its Z-score, you know where it falls relative to other apples.

Calculating Z-scores

Standard scores are a great way to understand where a specific observation falls relative to the entire distribution. They also allow you to take observations drawn from normally distributed populations that have different means and standard deviations and place them on a standard scale. This standard scale enables you to compare observations that would otherwise not be possible.

This process is called standardization, and it allows you to compare observations and calculate probabilities across different populations. In other words, it permits you to compare apples to oranges. Isn't statistics great!

To standardize your data, you need to convert the raw measurements into Z-scores.

To calculate the standard score for an observation, take the raw measurement, subtract the mean, and divide by the standard deviation. Mathematically, the formula for that process is the following:

$$Z = \frac{X - \mu}{\sigma}$$

X represents the raw value of the measurement of interest. Mu and sigma represent the parameters for the population from which the observation was drawn.

After standardizing your data, you can place them within the standard normal distribution. In this manner, standardization allows you to compare different types of observations based on where each observation falls within its own distribution.

Suppose we literally want to compare apples to oranges. Specifically, let's compare their weights. Imagine we have an apple that weighs 110 grams and an orange that weighs 100 grams.

If we compare the raw values, it's easy to see that the apple weighs more than the orange. However, let's compare their standard scores. To do this, we'll need to know the properties of the weight distributions for apples and oranges. Assume that the weights of apples and oranges follow a normal distribution with the following parameter values:

	Apples	**Oranges**
Mean weight grams	100	140
Standard deviation	15	25

Now let's calculate the Z-scores:

- Apple = (110-100) / 15 = 0.667
- Orange = (100-140) / 25 = -1.6

The Z-score for the apple (0.667) is positive, which means that our apple weighs more than the average apple. It's not an extreme value by any means, but it is above average for apples. On the other hand, the orange has a fairly negative Z-score (-1.6). It's pretty far below the mean weight for oranges. I've placed these Z-values in the standard normal distribution below.

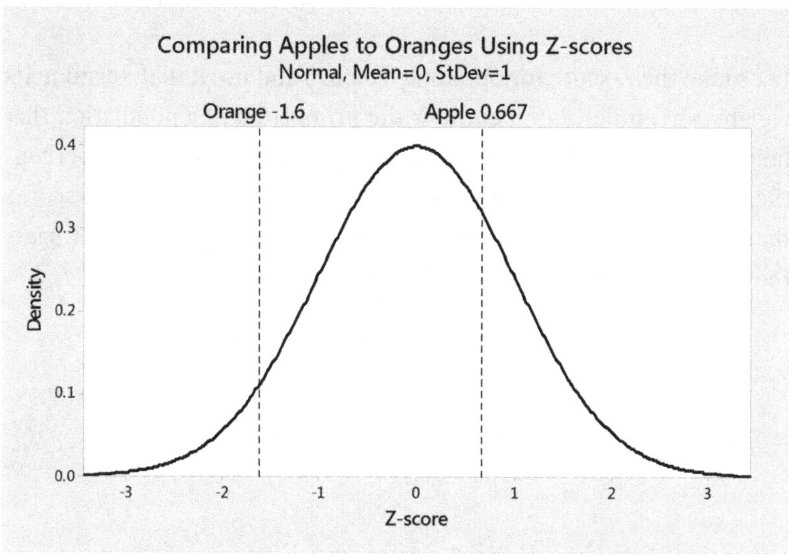

While our apple weighs more than our orange, we are comparing a somewhat heavier than average apple to a downright puny orange! Using Z-scores, we've learned how each fruit fits within its own distribution and how they compare to each other.

Using a Table of Z-scores

The normal distribution is a probability distribution. As with any probability distribution, the proportion of the area that falls under the curve between two points on a probability distribution plot indicates the probability that a value will fall within that interval.

Typically, I use statistical software to find areas under the curve. However, when you're working with the normal distribution and convert values to standard scores, you can calculate areas by looking up Z-scores in a Standard Normal Distribution Table.

Because there are an infinite number of different normal distributions, publishers can't print a table for each distribution. However, you can transform the values from any normal distribution into Z-scores, and then use a table of standard scores to calculate probabilities.

Let's take the Z-score for our apple (0.667) and use it to determine its weight percentile. A percentile is the proportion of a population that falls below a specific value. Consequently, to determine the percentile, we need to find the area that corresponds to the range of Z-scores that are less than 0.667. In the portion of the table on the next page, the closest Z-score to ours is 0.65, which we'll use.

z	Height	Area
0.00	39.89	0.00
0.05	39.84	3.99
0.10	39.69	7.97
0.15	39.45	11.92
0.20	39.10	15.85
0.25	38.67	19.74
0.30	38.14	23.58
0.35	37.52	27.37
0.40	36.83	31.08
0.45	36.05	34.73
0.50	35.21	38.29
0.55	34.29	41.77
0.60	33.32	45.15
0.65	32.30	48.43
0.70	31.23	51.61

The trick with these tables is using the values in conjunction with properties of the normal distribution to calculate probabilities that you need. The table value indicates that the area of the curve between -0.65 and +0.65 is 48.43%. However, that's not what we want to know. We want the area that is less than a Z-score of 0.65.

We know that the two halves of the normal distribution are mirror images of each other. So, if the area for the interval from -0.65 and +0.65 is 48.43%, then the range from 0 to +0.65 must be half of that: 48.43/2 = 24.215%. Additionally, we know that the area for all scores less than zero is half (50%) of the distribution.

Therefore, the area for all scores up to 0.65 = 50% + 24.215% = 74.215%

Our apple is at approximately the 74th percentile.

Below is a probability distribution plot produced by statistical software that shows the same percentile along with a graphical representation of the corresponding area under the curve. The value is slightly different because we used a Z-score of 0.65 from the table while the software uses the more precise value of 0.667.

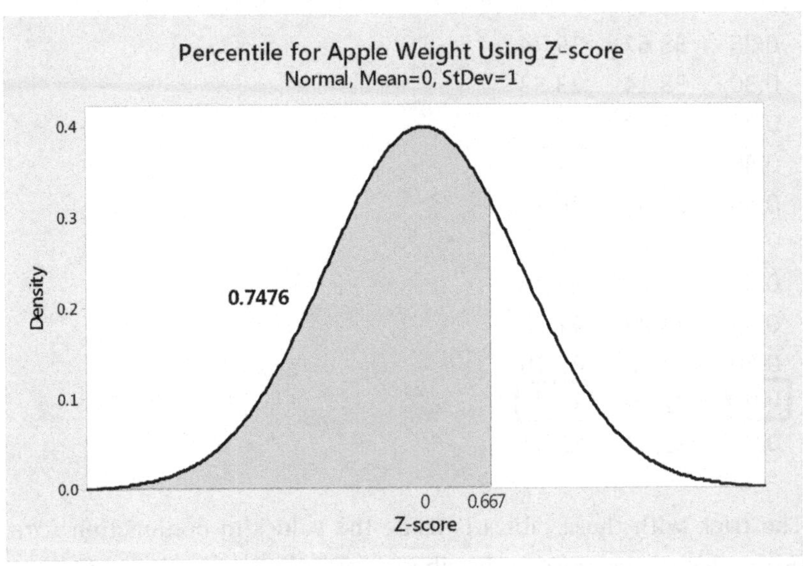

In chapter 3, you learned several different ways to calculate percentiles for values in a dataset. Now, you know how to use Z-scores to calculate percentiles for normal distributions! Additionally, the probability distribution method works for all continuous probability distributions—not just the normal distribution—as long as you know which distribution fits your data.

Why the Normal Distribution is Important

In addition to all the above, there are several other reasons why the normal distribution is crucial in statistics.

- Some statistical hypothesis tests assume that the data follow a normal distribution.

- Linear and nonlinear regression both assume that the residuals follow a normal distribution.
- The central limit theorem states that as the sample size increases, the sampling distribution of the mean follows a normal distribution even when the underlying distribution of the original variable is non-normal.

That was quite a bit about the normal distribution! Hopefully, you see that it is crucial because of the many ways that analysts use it.

Summary and Next Steps

Probability distributions are great tools when you need to understand the probabilities associated with values and ranges of values. These distributions apply to populations and use estimates for the population parameters.

You learned about discrete distributions with an emphasis on binary data.

Then we covered continuous data and saw examples of both skewed, non-normal distributions and the symmetric normal distribution. The normal distribution is fundamental in statistics because many phenomena follow it. Using the normal distribution, you learned about the Empirical Rule, how to calculate Z-scores to standardize data, and use a table of Z-scores to calculation percentiles.

In my book about hypothesis tests, I show you how probability distributions are the basis for hypothesis testing. Additionally, you'll learn how to test your data to determine which probability distribution best fits your sample data. For the population you're studying, you can identify the probability distribution that most likely produced the properties you observe in your random sample.

Probability distributions fall in the domain of inferential statistics for the following reasons:

- Analysts use representative samples to estimate the parameters of the population distribution.
- Probability distributions draw inferences about the probabilities of values in the population.

The next chapter explores the differences between descriptive and inferential statistics. We'll start diving into the concepts, procedures, and challenges associated with inferential statistics. Most of the rest of the book focuses on inferential statistics.

This set of methods is crucial for scientists because they aspire to make discoveries that apply beyond just their sample. For instance, experimenters do not want to test the effectiveness of a new medication on a sample of 50 individuals and then be able to apply the findings to only that small group! However, generalizing your results from a sample to a population requires that you understand certain concepts and implement various practices and procedures.

CHAPTER 5

Descriptive and Inferential Statistics

Descriptive and inferential statistics are two broad categories in the field of statistics. In this chapter, I show you how both types of statistics are essential for different purposes. Interestingly, while some of the statistical measures are similar, the goals and methodologies are very different.

Here's the difference in a nutshell:

- Descriptive statistics describe a dataset for a particular group of objects, observations, or people. They don't attempt to generalize beyond the set of observations.
- Inferential statistics use a dataset to make conclusions about the larger population from which the sample was drawn. These statistics generalize beyond the specific observations that are in the dataset to a larger group or population.

Descriptive Statistics

Both descriptive and inferential statistics help you make sense out of row after row of data!

Use descriptive statistics to summarize and graph the data for a group that you choose. This process allows you to understand that specific set of observations.

Descriptive statistics describe a sample. That's pretty straightforward. You simply take a group that you're interested in, record data about the group members, and then use summary statistics and graphs to present the group properties and relationships. With descriptive statistics, there is little uncertainty because you are describing only the people or items that you actually measure. You're not trying to infer properties about a larger population.

The process involves taking a potentially large number of data points in the sample and reducing them down to a few meaningful summary values and graphs. This procedure allows us to gain more insights and visualize the data than merely pouring through row upon row of raw numbers!

Descriptive statistics frequently use statistical measures that you should be very familiar with by now to describe a particular group:

Central tendency: Use the mean or the median to locate the center of the dataset. This measure tells you where most values fall.

Dispersion: How far out from the center do the data extend? You can use the range or standard deviation to measure the dispersion. Low dispersion indicates that values cluster more tightly around the center. Higher dispersion signifies that data points fall further away from the center. We can also graph the frequency distribution.

Skewness: The measure tells you whether the distribution of values is symmetric or skewed.

Correlation: The strength of the tendency for two variables to change together.

You can present this summary information using both numbers and graphs. These are the standard descriptive statistics, but there are other descriptive analyses you can perform. These techniques include assessing the relationships of paired data using correlation and scatterplots and graphing differences between groups using boxplots.

Example of Descriptive Statistics

Suppose we want to describe the test scores in a specific class of 30 students. We record all of the test scores and calculate the summary statistics and produce graphs. Obtain the CSV data file from my website: Descriptive_statistics.csv.

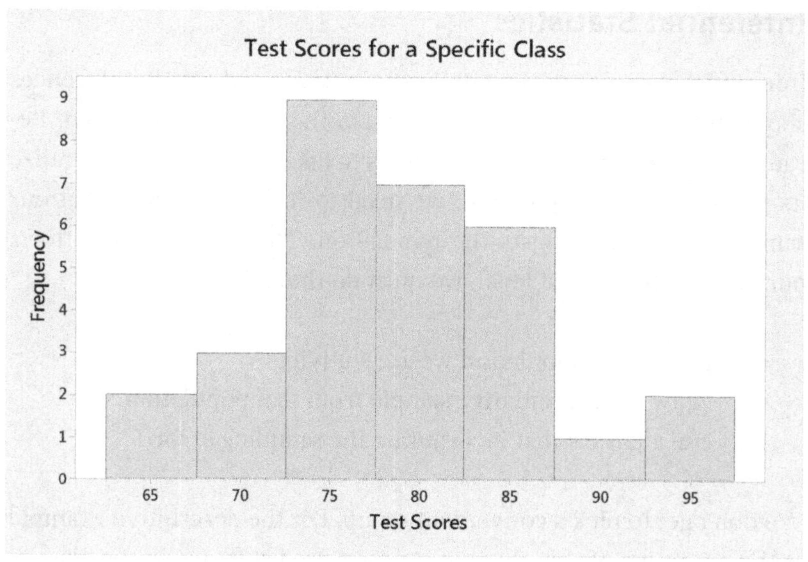

Statistic	Class value
Mean	79.18
Standard deviation	7.76
Proportion >= 70	86.7%

These results indicate that the mean score of this class is 79.18. The scores range from 66.21 to 96.53, and the distribution is symmetrically centered around the mean. A score of at least 70 on the test is acceptable. The data show that 86.7% of the students have acceptable scores.

Collectively, this information gives us a pretty good picture of this specific class. The process was very straightforward. We simply recorded the test scores for everyone in the class. There is no uncertainty surrounding these statistics because we gathered the scores for everyone in the class. However, we can't take these results and extrapolate to a larger population of students.

Inferential Statistics

Inferential statistics takes data from a sample and makes inferences about the larger population from which the sample was drawn. Because the goal of inferential statistics is to take a sample and generalize its properties to a population, we need to have confidence that our sample accurately reflects the population. This requirement affects our process. At a broad level, we must do the following:

1. Define the population we are studying.
2. Draw a representative sample from that population.
3. Use analyses that incorporate the sampling error.

We don't get to pick a convenient group. For the descriptive example at the beginning of this chapter, we measured students in the class in which we were interested. However, selecting students becomes more complex for inferential statistics. Using a handy class is unlikely to produce a representative sample.

Instead, we need a sampling procedure that tends to produce a sample that accurately reflects the population from which you draw it. Random sampling is a procedure that allows us to have confidence that the sample represents the population. The random nature of this process helps avoid any systematic bias that would invalidate our results.

Random sampling is a primary method for obtaining samples that mirrors the population on average. This type of sampling produces statistics, such as the mean, that are not systematically too high or too low. In other words, the critical characteristic of random samples is that they produce sample statistics that tend to be correct on average.

Consequently, when we obtain a random sample, we can generalize from the sample to the broader population. Unfortunately, gathering a genuinely random sample can be a complicated process. Yeah, I know, the word "random" makes it sound simple and half-hazard, but a random sample can be challenging to collect! Later sections in this chapter describe several random sampling methodologies.

Pros and Cons of Working with Samples

In most cases, it is simply impossible to measure the entire population to understand its properties. The alternative is to gather a random sample and then use the methodologies of inferential statistics to analyze the sample data.

While samples are much more practical and less expensive to work with, there are tradeoffs. Typically, we learn about the population by drawing a relatively small sample from it. We are a very long way off from measuring all people or objects in that population. Consequently, when you estimate the properties of a population from a sample, the sample statistics are unlikely to equal the actual population value exactly. For instance, your sample mean is unlikely to equal the population mean exactly.

Sampling error is the difference between the sample statistic and the population value. Inferential statistics incorporate estimates of this error into the statistical results.

In contrast, summary values in descriptive statistics are straightforward. The average score in a specific class is a known value because we measured all individuals in that class. There is little uncertainty.

To gain the benefits of inferential statistics, you must understand the relationship between populations, subpopulations, population parameters, samples, and sample statistics.

Populations

Populations can include people, but other examples include objects, events, businesses, and so on. In statistics, there are two general types of populations.

Populations can be the complete set of all similar items that exist. For example, the population of a country includes all people currently living within that country. It's a finite but potentially extensive list of members.

However, a population can be a theoretical construct that is potentially infinite in size. For example, quality improvement analysts often consider all current and future output from a manufacturing line to be part of a population.

Populations share a set of attributes that you define. For example, the following are populations:

- Stars in the Milky Way galaxy.
- Parts from a production line.
- Citizens of the United States.
- 8th grade students in the State of Pennsylvania.

Before you begin a study, you must carefully define the population that you are studying. These populations can be narrowly defined to meet the needs of your analysis.

For example, your population can be adult Swedish women who are otherwise healthy but have osteoporosis.

Subpopulations

Subpopulations share additional attributes. For instance, the population of the United States contains the subpopulations of men and women. You can also subdivide it in other ways such as region, age, socioeconomic status, and so on. Different studies that involve the same population can divide it into different subpopulations depending on what makes sense for the data and the analyses.

Understanding the subpopulations in your study helps you grasp the subject matter more thoroughly. They can also help you produce statistical models that fit the data better. Subpopulations are particularly important when they have characteristics that are systematically different than the overall population. When you analyze your data, you need to be aware of these deeper divisions. In fact, you can treat the relevant subpopulations as additional factors in later analyses.

Let's revisit an example we looked at in the section about histograms. Now assume we're conducting a scientific study of the height of full-grown, adult, American citizens. Let's further assume that we don't know much about the subject. Because we can't possibly measure in the population, we'll need to use inferential statistics to use a sample to learn about the population. We collect a random sample, measure the heights in centimeters, and calculate the sample mean and standard deviation. Download the CSV data file from my website to try this yourself: Heights.csv.

Because we gathered a random sample, we can assume that the sample statistics are unbiased estimates of the population parameters.

Now, suppose we learn more about the study area and include male and female as subpopulations. We obtain the following results.

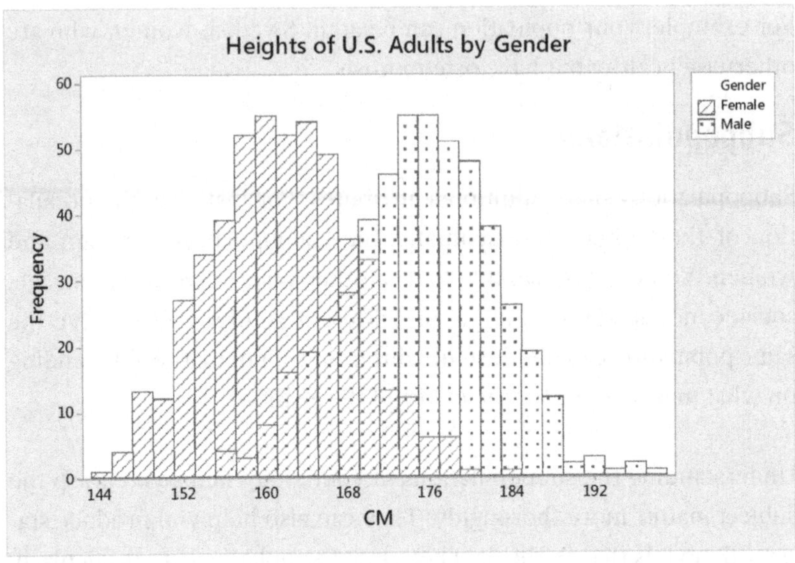

During this process, we learn that gender is a crucial subpopulation that relates to height and increases our understanding of the subject matter. In future studies about height, we can include gender as a variable. That's how scientists think about research questions and add to their knowledge.

This example is intentionally easy to understand but imagine a study about a less obvious subject. This process helps you gain new insights and produce better statistical models.

Population Parameters versus Sample Statistics

A parameter is a value that describes a characteristic of an entire population, such as the population mean. Because you can rarely measure a population as a whole, you usually don't know the real value of a parameter. Consequently, parameter values are nearly always unknowable. While we can't measure the parameter value, it exists.

For example, the average height of adult women in the United States is a parameter that has an exact value—we just don't know what it is! While we'll never know the precise value of these population parameters, we can use inferential statistics to estimate them and incorporate a margin of error.

The population mean and standard deviation are two common parameters. In statistics, Greek symbols usually represent population parameters, such as μ (mu) for the mean and σ (sigma) for the standard deviation.

A statistic is a characteristic of a sample. If you collect a sample and calculate the mean and standard deviation, these are sample statistics. Inferential statistics allow you to use sample statistics to make conclusions about a population. However, to draw valid conclusions, you must use random sampling techniques, as discussed earlier.

Type	Population Parameter	Sample Statistic
Mean	Mu (μ)	$\bar{x}$ (x-bar)
Standard deviation	Sigma (σ)	s
Correlation	Rho (ρ)	r

In inferential statistics, sample statistics are estimates of population parameters. For example, if we collect a random sample of adult women in the United States and measure their heights, we can calculate the sample mean and standard deviation and use them as unbiased estimates of the population parameters.

You can calculate the following types of estimates for population parameters:

Point estimates: These estimates use the sample data to produce a single value that is the most likely value for the population parameter. Sample statistics, such as the mean, are typically the point estimate for the population. Unfortunately, point estimates are always wrong by an unknown amount because of random sampling error.

Interval estimates: A range of values that likely contains the value of the population parameter. These intervals include a margin of error around the point estimate to account for random sampling error.

In short, point estimates are the best guess value but are guaranteed to be wrong by at least a little bit because you're working with a sample that is small in comparison to the population. Interval estimates are ranges of values that probably contain the parameter value. I'll show you these in action later in this chapter!

In this book, you first encountered the term "parameter" in chapter 4 in the context of probability distribution plots. After estimating population parameters from a representative sample, you can input the parameter estimates into a probability function and, voila, estimate probabilities for values and ranges of values. While it goes beyond the scope of this book, probability distributions are at the heart of hypothesis testing and confidence intervals.

Tools for Inferential Statistics

Inferential methods can produce similar summary values as descriptive statistics, such as the mean and standard deviation. However, as I'll show you, we use them very differently when making inferences.

I'll touch upon hypothesis tests, confidence intervals, and regression analysis briefly. This book discusses these tools only in a very general sense. You'll learn a bit more about these procedures throughout the rest of this book, but we won't get into the nuts and bolts of how they work. For now, you only need to understand the general purpose of these tools.

Hypothesis tests

Hypothesis tests use sample data to answer questions about point estimates, such as the following:

- Is the population mean greater than or less than a particular value?
- Are the means of two or more populations different from each other?

Suppose we study the effectiveness of a new medication by comparing the outcomes in a treatment and control group. Hypothesis tests can tell us whether the drug's effect, which is the mean difference between the treatment and the control group, that we observe in the sample is likely to exist in the population. It's possible that the sample effect is random error rather than a real effect. After all, we don't want to use the medication if it is effective only in our specific sample.

Instead, we need evidence that it'll be useful in the entire population of patients. Hypothesis tests allow us to draw these types of conclusions about whole populations.

For example, is the proportion of flu cases among the vaccinated different than the unvaccinated?

Confidence intervals (CIs)

In inferential statistics, a primary goal is to estimate population parameters. These parameters are the unknown values for the entire population, such as the population mean and standard deviation. These parameter values are not only unknown but almost always unknowable. The sampling error I mentioned earlier produces uncertainty, or a margin of error, around our estimates.

Suppose we define our population as all high school basketball players. Then, we draw a random sample from this population and calculate the mean height of 181 cm. This sample estimate of 181 cm is our point estimate of the mean height of the population. However, it's virtually guaranteed that our estimate of the population parameter is not exactly correct.

Confidence intervals incorporate the uncertainty and sample error to create a range of values the actual population value is likely to fall within. For example, a confidence interval of [176 186] indicates we can be confident that the real population mean falls within this range.

Regression analysis

Regression analysis describes the relationship between a set of independent variables and a dependent variable. This analysis incorporates hypothesis tests that help determine whether the relationships we observe in the sample data also exist in the population.

For example, the fitted line plot below displays the relationship in the regression model between height and weight in adolescent girls. Because the relationship is statistically significant, we have sufficient evidence to conclude that this relationship exists in the population rather than just our sample.

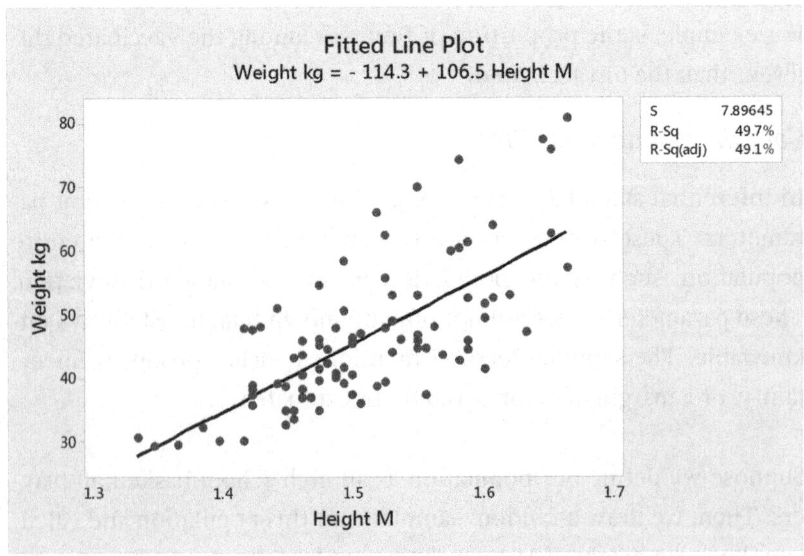

Properties of Good Estimates

Our goal is to draw a random sample from a population and use it to estimate the properties of that population. While we'll never know the actual population parameters, we want our sample to produce good estimates of them.

What properties do the best estimates have?

Suppose you request an estimate—say for the cost of a service that you are considering. How would you define a reasonable estimate?

The estimates should tend to be right on target. They should not be systematically too high or too low. In other words, they should be unbiased or correct on average.

Recognizing that estimates are almost never exactly correct, you want to minimize the discrepancy between the estimated value and actual value. Large differences are bad!

Unbiased estimates with a small amount of error are what we need!

How do you obtain estimates with these properties?

Random sampling helps you obtain unbiased estimates.

Your sample size and the variability in the population determine the size of the error.

The upcoming sections of this chapter look at these issues in more detail.

Sample Size and Margins of Error

I'm sure you've heard that having a large sample size is a good thing. In this section, you'll learn why!

Here's some shocking information for you—sample statistics are *always* wrong! When you use samples to estimate the properties of populations, you never obtain the correct values exactly. Don't worry. I'll help you navigate this issue using a simple statistical tool!

For example, when we read survey results, we are not learning about just the opinions of those who responded to the survey, but about an entire population. Or, when we see averages, such as health measures and salaries, we're learning about them on the scale of a population, not just the few subjects in a study. Consequently, inferential statistics can provide valuable information.

Inferential statistics is a powerful tool because it allows you to use a relatively small sample to learn about an entire population. However, to have any chance of obtaining good results, you must follow sampling procedures that help your sample to represent the population faithfully.

Unfortunately, even when you diligently follow the proper methodology for performing a valid study, your estimates will almost always be at least a little wrong. I'm not referring to unscrupulous manipulation, mistakes, or methodology errors. I'm talking about cases where researchers use the correct sampling methodology and legitimate statistical calculations to produce the best possible estimates.

Why does this happen? Random error is present in all samples. By sheer chance alone, your sample contains error that causes the statistics to be off by at least a little bit. Your data are not 100% representative of the population because they are not the entire population! Samples never provide a perfect depiction of the population from which it is drawn.

All estimates are at least a little wrong, but sometimes they can be very wrong. Unfortunately, the media and other sources forget this point when they present statistics. Upon seeing an estimate, you should wonder—how large is the difference between the estimate and the actual population value? What is the margin of error?

The margin of error relates to the sample size. Let's explore why larger samples are better.

The primary goal of inferential statistics is to generalize from a sample to a population. To accomplish this objective, the sample must be similar to the population. The simple truth is that it's more difficult for a small sample to approximate an entire population closely. Larger samples tend to better represent the full complexities of a population.

Additionally, larger sample sizes help you avoid unusual samples. Think about coin tosses. You expect to obtain heads 50% of the time. If you have four coin tosses, it is not surprising to get heads 3 out of 4 times (75%). That's a considerable distance from 50%—but it's just one extra heads. However, if you have 100 coin tosses, it's improbable that you'd get heads 75% of the time. It's possible, but you'd need very fluky luck to get those 25 extra heads (50 + 25 = 75).

The same thing occurs when you're drawing a random sample. Imagine you're conducting an IQ study. You'll obtain a random sample of people and measure their IQs. If you have a sample of five people, just one unusually high or low IQ score will throw off the mean. However, if you have a sample size of 50, a few unusual scores won't impact the mean much.

The next section explains sampling distributions, which illustrate how sample sizes relate to margin error.

Sampling Distributions of the Mean

A vital concept in inferential statistics is that the particular random sample that you draw for a study is just one of a large number of possible samples that you could have pulled from your population of interest. Understanding this broader context of all possible samples and how your study's sample fits within it provides valuable information.

Suppose we draw a substantial number of random samples of the same size from the same population and calculate the sample mean for each sample. During this process, we'd observe a broad spectrum of sample means, and we can graph their distribution.

By using simulation software, you can see this in action. Imagine that you obtain random samples of people and measure their IQs. We'll assume the distribution of IQ scores in the population follows a normal distribution that has a mean of 100 and a standard deviation of 15. These parameters define the properties of the distribution from which we'll be drawing random samples. Now, imagine we're hyperactive researchers and that instead of obtaining one sample, we'll collect hundreds of thousands!

Here's our process. We'll start with a sample size of five and draw 500,000 random samples of that size. That gives us 500,000 samples with five IQ scores in each sample. For each of those samples, we'll calculate the average IQ and plot them on a histogram. Then we'll follow the same process for a sample size of 20 and 60.

Statisticians refer to this type of distribution as a sampling distribution of the mean. These are distributions of sample means for samples of a particular size that you draw from a population with specific properties. These distributions represent the idea of conducting the same experiment many times and observing the distribution of sample means. Sampling distributions also exist for other population properties such as the standard deviation, median, and proportion.

The histogram displays the sampling distributions for our repeated IQ study. The bars are tiny because we collected 500,000 samples of each size! Keep in mind that these distributions represent the distribution of sample means rather than individual scores.

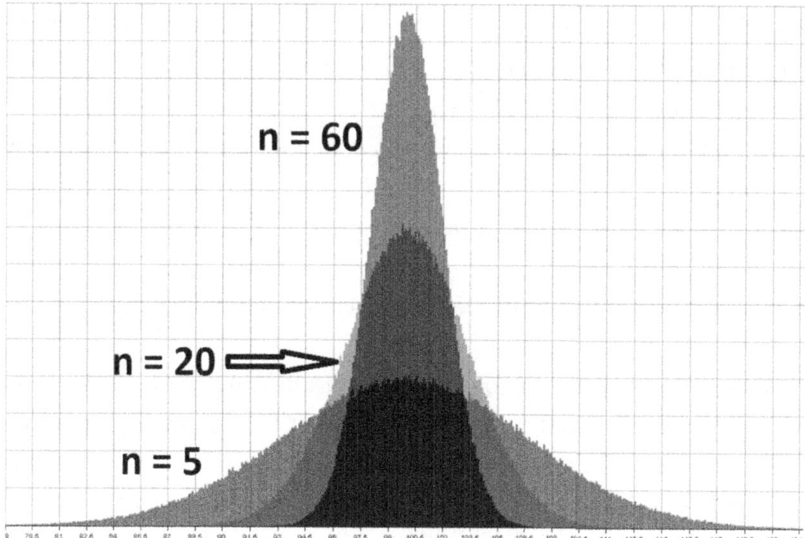

The first thing to notice is that all three distributions center on the population's mean IQ of 100 and they are distributed symmetrically around that mean. These properties indicate that the sample means are unbiased because they are not systematically too high or too low. Stated another way, samples have an equal probability of being too high or too low. They're correct on average. That's good! These sample means are unbiased because the simulation used random sampling.

However, the spreads of the distributions are clearly different. The variability of these distributions reflects the amount of sampling error associated with different sample sizes.

Let's start with the distribution for a sample size of five, which is the widest. While this distribution centers on 100, the broader spread indicates that a greater percentage of sample means will fall further away from the population value in the center and instead be out in the tails. Consequently, obtaining a sample mean as low as 88 or as high as 112 is not surprising when the sample size is five. In fact, you could get even higher or lower means; it's just less likely.

Suppose you obtain a sample mean of 110. You must have had a fluky luck of the draw and collected several unusually high IQ scores that affected your small sample. The wider spread of this distribution shows that you are more likely to obtain an unusual sample mean with a small sample size. In other words, it is less likely that your sample mean is close to the actual population value.

Estimates from smaller samples have a larger margin of error.

Now, let's look at the narrowest distribution, which represents samples of size 60. It's still centered on 100, but the narrow distribution indicates that you are unlikely to obtain sample means far from 100. It would be implausible to obtain sample means less than 95 or higher than 105. Most sample means are packed close to the population value in the center while few are out in the tails. The narrower spread of this distribution shows that you are less likely to obtain an unusual sample mean when you have a large sample size. In other words, you have more confidence that your sample mean is close to the actual population value.

Estimates from larger samples have a smaller margin of error.

The distribution for samples of size 20 has a width that is in-between the other two.

The wider distributions for small sample sizes indicate your sample mean has a higher probability of falling further away from the population mean. As you increase the sample size, the sampling distributions tighten up, which signifies you can be more confident that the sample mean is relatively close to the population mean. For example, with a sample size of 60, your sample mean is probably at most a few IQ points away from the actual population mean of 100.

In statistics, we refer to this concept as the precision of the estimates. More precise estimates have smaller margins of error around the estimate. Conversely, less precise estimates have larger margins of error and provide a vaguer idea about a population's characteristics. You want greater precision because you'll have better information about the actual value of the population parameter.

Precision is a function of both the variability in the population and the size of the sample. However, we can usually control only the sample size in our studies. Consequently, increasing the sample size is *the* method to use improve the precision of your sample estimates.

Fortunately, for real studies, you don't need to collect many samples. Statistical procedures can estimate the sampling distribution from a single sample. Aren't statistics great! These sampling distributions are a special type of probability distribution and are at the core of hypothesis testing and confidence intervals. While those procedures are beyond the scope of this book, I want to take a quick look at how you can use confidence intervals to assess the precision of sample estimates. They give us an idea of how wrong our sample estimate might be.

Note: The simulation software I used is Statistics 101. It is giftware that is free to use, but they ask for donations. You can find the link to this software and the script I created for the IQ example on my website.

Confidence Intervals and Precision

Confidence intervals help you assess the precision of your estimates. While working with hundreds of thousands of samples in the simulation was fun, let's see how you assess precision for individual samples. We'll again use an IQ study to illustrate this point. This time I'll have my statistical software draw a sample of size 10 and another of size 100 from the same population we used for the simulations. We'll use confidence intervals to compare the precision of the estimates for both samples.

Here's how the distribution of IQ scores in the population appears on a normal probability distribution plot.

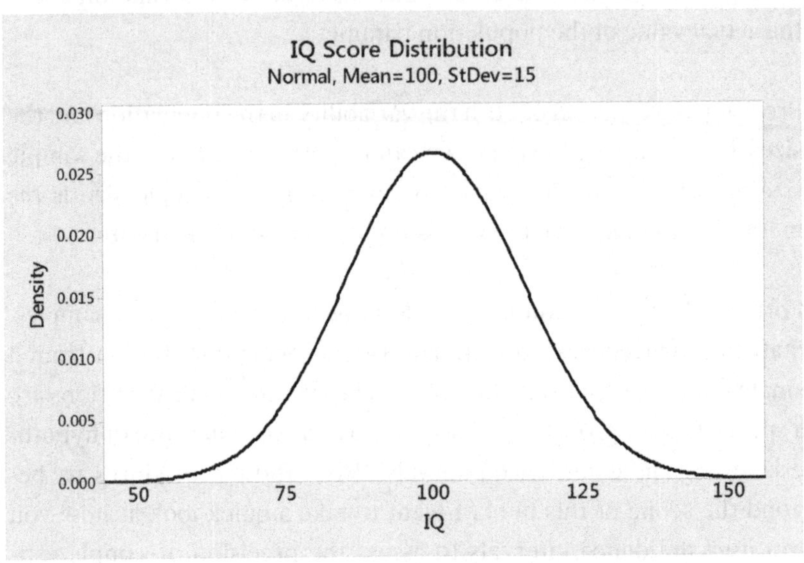

Download the CSV data file from my website: SimulatedIQData.csv. Or, use statistical software to create different sized random samples and try it yourself!

Example: Sample Statistics and CIs for 10 Observations

For the sample size of 10, here are the summary statistics for my random sample.

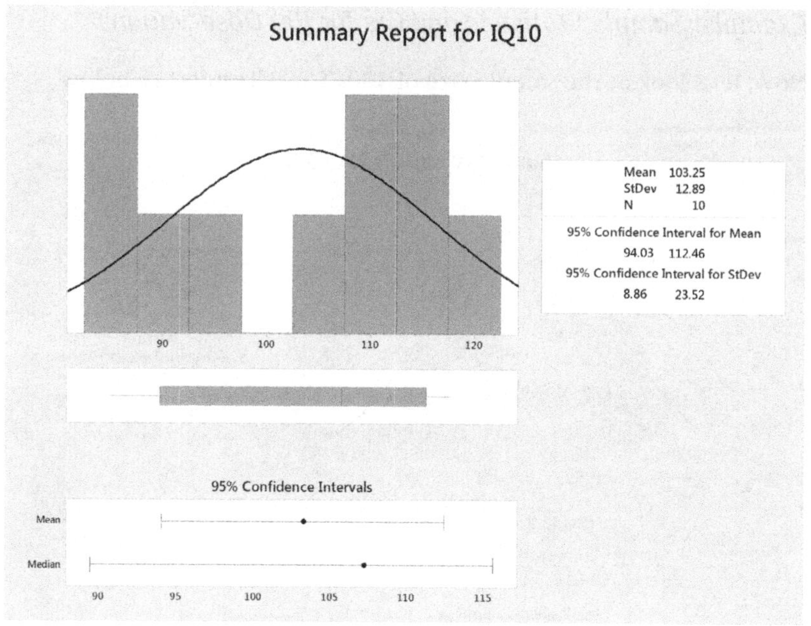

Statisticians usually consider a sample size of 10 to be a bit on the small side. From the histogram, the data do not look much like the original population. The estimates for the mean and standard deviation are 103.25 and 12.89, respectively. They are the point estimates for the population parameters, which are both in the right ballpark for the correct values of 100 and 15.

We have our point estimates, but we know that those aren't exactly correct. Let's check the confidence intervals to see the ranges for where the actual parameter values are likely to fall.

The confidence interval for the mean is [94.03 112.46], and for the standard deviation it is [8.86 23.52]. The population parameters usually fall within their confidence intervals. Typically, we don't know the actual parameter values, but for this illustration we can see that both estimates fall within their intervals. The sample does not provide an exact representation of the population, but the estimates are not too far off. If we didn't know the actual values, the CIs would give us useful guidance.

Example: Sample Statistics and CIs for 100 Observations

Now, let's look at the sample size of 100. Those results are below.

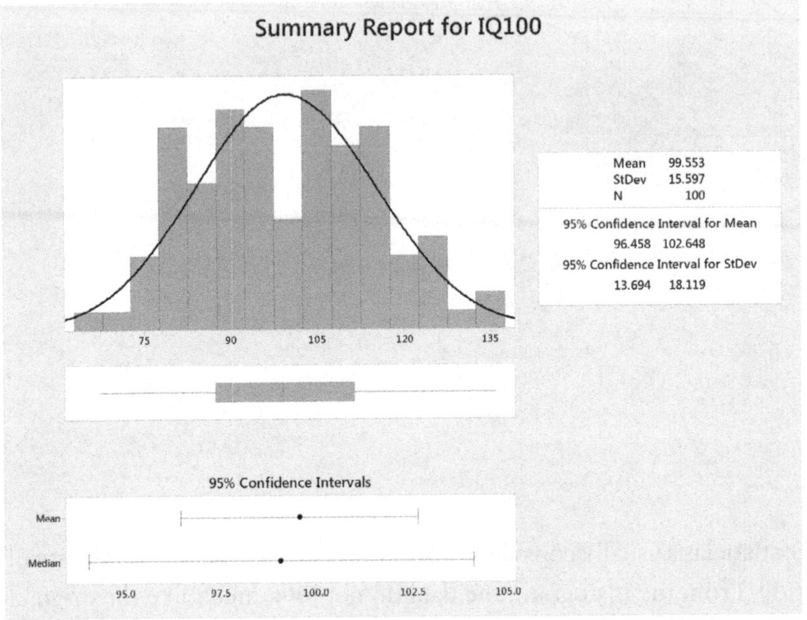

For this larger sample, this histogram is beginning to look more like the underlying population distribution. The estimates for the mean and standard deviation are 99.553 and 15.597, respectively. Both of these point estimates are closer to the actual population values than their counterparts in the smaller sample.

For the confidence intervals, both of the CIs again contain the parameters. However, notice that these intervals are tighter than for the sample size of 10. For example, the CI for the mean is [96.458 102.648] compared to [94.03 112.46] for the sample size of 10. That's a range of about 6 IQ points rather than 18. The tighter intervals indicate that these estimates are more precise than those from the smaller sample. In other words, the difference between the sample estimate and actual parameter value is likely to be smaller for the larger sample.

Narrower confidence intervals represent more precise estimates.

In summary, use confidence intervals to evaluate the precision of your sample estimates. If your intervals are too broad to be meaningful, you'll need to increase your sample size.

Random Sampling Methodologies

In statistics, sampling refers to selecting a subset of a population. After drawing the sample, you measure one or more characteristics of all items in the sample, such as height, income, temperature, opinion, etc. If you want to generalize these characteristics from the sample to the whole population, it imposes restrictions on how you collect the sample. If you use an incorrect methodology, the sample might not represent the population, which can lead you to erroneous conclusions.

When a researcher intentionally picks people to include in their sample, it's likely their choices will somehow skew the sample based on their preferences and convenience. The biases that the researcher introduces might be entirely unintended.

A sample based on convenience is a prime example of what not to do. This process occurs when researchers recruit subjects who are easier to obtain. For example, imagine that a researcher goes to a local mall to recruit study participants who should represent an entire state. These shoppers are likely to have demographic characteristics, incomes, and other attributes that are more similar each other than the overall state population.

Most inferential statistical procedures assume that you have a random sample. Randomness helps ensure that you obtain a sample that accurately represents the population. Nonrandom methodologies are prone to produce unreliable estimates of the population parameters.

While sampling methodologies can cover an entire book, I'll highlight several fundamental methods that illustrate some of the issues, approaches, and goals.

The following random sampling approaches minimize bias, but they do not indicate that your sample statistics exactly equal the population parameters. Instead, estimates from a specific sample are likely to be a bit high or low, but the process produces accurate estimates on average. Random sampling can yield samples that don't represent the population—it's just not the expected result.

Additionally, random sampling might sound a bit haphazard and easy to do—both of which are not true. Random sampling often requires a lot of planning and work!

Simple Random Sampling

The most well-known method to obtain an unbiased, representative sample is simple random sampling. With this method, all items in the population have an equal probability of being selected, and there is no connection between those who researchers include in the sample. This process helps ensure that the sample contains the full range of the population. Additionally, all relevant subpopulations should be incorporated into the sample and represented accurately on average. Simple random sampling minimizes the bias and simplifies data analysis.

Typically, simple random sampling requires that you have a complete roster for the population, and then you randomly choose participants from that list. However, depending upon your population, it can be challenging to obtain that complete list! And, you might have other constraints.

For example, earlier in this chapter, I presented an example of assessing a standardized test that 8th graders in the State of Pennsylvania take. To conduct a simple random sample, we'd need a list of all 8th

grade students in the state and then randomly choose from that list without regard to which school they attend.

Stratified Sampling

Use stratified sampling to ensure that you obtain precise population estimates for relevant subpopulations (strata) in your population. The method ensures specific subgroups are present in the sample with a sufficient sample size for these groups. Strata are subpopulations whose members are relatively similar to each other compared to the broader population. Researchers can create strata based on income, gender, and race among many other possibilities. For example, if your research question required you to compare outcomes between income levels, you might base the strata on income.

Stratified sampling involves multiple steps. First, break down the population into strata. From each stratum, use simple random sampling to draw a fixed sample size. This process ensures that you obtain a specific number of observations per stratum, which produces precise estimates for all strata and facilitates comparisons between them.

For example, let's go back to our standardized testing example. Suppose our research requires us to compare test scores by income. We can use income level for our strata. Students from households with similar incomes should be relatively similar compared to the overall state population.

While we want a random sample for unbiased estimates overall, we also want to ensure that we obtain precise estimates for each income level in our population. If we use simple random sampling, income levels with a small number of students and random chance could conspire to provide small sample sizes for some income levels. These smaller sample sizes produce relatively imprecise estimates for them.

To counter this problem, we decide to use stratified sampling. Our sampling plan might dictate that we'll select 100 students from each income level using simple random sampling. Of course, this plan presupposes that we know the household income level for each student, which might be problematic.

The benefit of stratified sampling is that you obtain reasonably precise estimates for all subgroups that relate to your research question. The drawback is that analyzing these datasets is more complicated. When you use stratified random sampling, you can't simply take the overall sample average and use it for the overall population mean because you know that the smaller strata are overrepresented.

Cluster Sampling

Use cluster sampling as a cost savings alternative to other methods. Clusters are groups that mirror the diversity of the whole population. Additionally, clusters are like each other. Because clusters reflect the population and are themselves comparable, researchers do not need to obtain samples from all clusters, which simplifies the process. Researchers choose the clusters randomly and then either use simple random sampling to pick subjects from the selected clusters or use entire clusters.

Geographic clusters are the most common type of clusters. The rationale for using them is that it is impractical to obtain samples from wide-ranging geographic regions. Cluster sampling reduces the geographic areas from which you recruit subjects.

For example, imagine we are studying rural communities in a state. Simple random sampling requires us to travel to all these communities, which could be cost and time prohibitive. However, we can divide rural communities into similar clusters. Then, we pick the community clusters randomly. After we have a set of randomly chosen clusters, we can use simple random sampling to select subjects from them.

The benefit of cluster sampling is that we don't need to travel to all geographic regions, only a randomly selected subset. However, like stratified sampling, the drawback is that analyzing clustered datasets is more complicated.

Example of Inferential Statistics

In the descriptive statistics section at the start of this chapter, I detailed a study about test scores for a specific class. We'll close the chapter by performing an inferential statistics study for that same test. By using the same test, but with the new goal of drawing inferences about a population, I can show you how that changes the way we conduct the study and the results we present.

In descriptive statistics, we picked the specific class that we wanted to describe and recorded all of the test scores for that class. We then calculated the exact mean, standard deviation, and passing proportion for that class. Nice and simple.

For inferential statistics, we need to define the population and then draw a random sample from that population.

Let's define our population as 8th-grade students in public schools in the State of Pennsylvania in the United States. We need to devise a random sampling plan to help ensure a representative sample. This process can be quite arduous. For the sake of this example, assume we are provided a list of names by the state for the entire population of 8th grade students. From this list, we use a simple random procedure to select 100 students. Note that these students will not be in one class, but from many different classes in different schools across the state. We'll be travelling all over the state to get their test scores!

For inferential statistics, we can calculate the point estimate for the mean, standard deviation, and proportion for our random sample. However, it is staggeringly improbable that any of these point estimates are precisely correct, and there is no way to know for sure anyway. Because we can't measure all subjects in this population, there is a margin of error around these statistics. Consequently, I'll report the confidence intervals for the mean, standard deviation, and the proportion of satisfactory scores (>=70). From my website, use the CSV data file: Inferential_statistics.csv.

Statistic	Population Parameter Estimate (CIs)
Mean	77.4 – 80.9
Standard deviation	7.7 – 10.1
Proportion scores >= 70	77% – 92%

Given the uncertainty associated with these estimates, we can be confident that the population mean is between 77.4 and 80.9. The population standard deviation is likely to fall between 7.7 and 10.1. And the population proportion of satisfactory scores is expected to be between 77% and 92%.

Summary and Next Steps

In this chapter, you learned how the difference between descriptive and inferential statistics lies in the process as much as it does the statistics that you report.

For descriptive statistics, we choose a group we want to describe and then measure all subjects in that group. Outside of measurement error, the statistical summary describes this group with complete certainty.

A study using descriptive statistics is simpler to perform. However, if you need evidence that an effect or relationship between variables exists in an entire population rather than only your sample, you need to use inferential statistics.

Inferential statistics use many of the same summary statistics and graphs as descriptive statistics. However, now you need to think about sampling methodologies, representative samples, point estimates, and margins of error. Additionally, the statistical results incorporate the uncertainty inherent when using a sample to understand an entire population.

For inferential statistics, you need to define the population. Then devise a random sampling methodology to help ensure that you obtain a representative sample that produces unbiased estimates. Unbiased estimates are not systematically too high or too low. Representative samples allow you generalize from the sample to the population.

Increasing the sample size tends to improve the precision of the estimates. In other words, you can expect the sampling error to be smaller when you use a larger sample.

Use confidence intervals to estimate the range of likely values for the population parameters. If this range is too broad to be meaningful, increase your sample size!

As you get into hypothesis testing, sufficiently large sample sizes are vital because they give tests a greater ability to detect differences between groups. This improved capability occurs thanks to the increased precision. Less precise estimates hamper the test's ability to determine whether groups are different.

As we move forward, the book focuses on using statistics in scientific studies. Scientific studies invariably use inferential statistics. There is little value to science in determining whether an effect exists only in a sample rather than the entire population. Whether the study is about medication effectiveness or an opinion poll, the findings are unimportant if they apply only to the specific group of subjects in the study. To be a valuable addition to science, the results must generalize beyond that small group. Consequently, the rest of this book stays with inferential statistics.

As you will learn, using statistics to answer scientific questions in an experiment requires a design that mitigates a variety of complications. Consequently, including statistical analyses in the scientific method requires yet another layer of knowledge about processes and procedures.

CHAPTER 6

Statistics in Scientific Studies

The scientific method is a proven procedure for expanding knowledge through experimentation and analysis. It is a process that uses careful planning, rigorous methodology, and thorough assessment. Statistical analysis plays an essential role in this process.

When you're talking about scientific studies or experiments, you're invariably using inferential statistics. Science doesn't generally care if an effect exists only in the sample.

In an experiment that includes statistical analysis, the analysis is at the end of a long series of events. To obtain valid results, it's crucial that you carefully plan and conduct a scientific study for all steps up to and including the analysis. In this chapter, I map out five steps for scientific studies that include statistical analyses.

It's vital that you understand the scientific method and know how to design a scientifically rigorous study that includes statistical analysis. Mistakes along the way can invalidate the results of your analysis. I've divided the process into five stages. Depending on the nature of your experiment, you might need to emphasize or deemphasize certain aspects.

For example, studies of physical phenomena will look very different than those in the social sciences. In the same vein, studies that use designed factorial experiments, observational studies, and surveys will all look different from each other. While studies can differ drastically, they all use aspects of the same roadmap I lay out.

This roadmap relates to scientific studies that include statistical analysis. However, even purely qualitative studies will share many of the same steps.

The steps in a scientifically rigorous study are the following:

1. Research Phase.
   - Define the Problem and Research Question.
   - Literature Review.
2. Operationalize Phase.
   - Define your variables and measurement techniques.
   - Design the experimental methods and determine sample size.
3. Data Collection.
4. Statistically analyze data and draw conclusions.
5. Communicate the results.

Step 1: Research Your Study Area

Good scientific research depends on gathering a lot of information before you even start collecting data. You'll need to investigate your subject-area to write a research question that your study can reasonably answer. Then, you'll need to develop in-depth knowledge about other studies to devise a plan for conducting your study.

Define Your Research Question

The first step of your study is to formulate a research question. This is the question you want your study to answer. Research questions focus your experiment, help guide your decision-making process, and helps prevent side issues from distracting you from your goal.

Typically, researchers start with a broad topic and research the subject area. Determine what types of questions researchers have and have not answered. This process helps to narrow the broad topic down to a more specific research question. Determine what studies researchers have already performed and what literature already exists. Will you answer a new question or try to replicate previous research? If you're trying to replicate previous results, will your study address any weaknesses identified in previous experiments?

Your research question should be appropriate for your discipline. Consequently, the properties of suitable research questions vary significantly by subject area. For example, acceptable research questions look different for physics, psychology, biology, and political science. However, they have some common qualities.

Research questions must be clear and concise. Readers of your short research question should clearly understand the goal of your study. Additionally, ensure the scope of the inquiry is narrow enough that your research can reasonably answer it using available time and resources.

Typically, developing your research question often starts with a topic that you are interested in and involves some initial research. This preliminary research helps you craft an actionable research question. However, after you devise your question, you'll need to conduct a much more in-depth review of the literature. And, you will likely perform some iterative fine-tuning. During the literature review, you might find yourself tweaking the research question.

Literature Review

A literature review is a very extensive background investigation into your research question. There are two primary goals of a literature review for a scientific study that involves statistical analysis.

First, you need to understand fully the subject-area that contains your research question. What have other studies found? Identify the significant relationships and effects that the literature recognizes along with their size and direction. What variables and factors play a role?

In short, define the current state of scientific knowledge surrounding your research question. This process helps you determine how your study fits within the field, enables you to understand the thought processes behind similar studies, and provides you with a general sense of the findings thus far.

Secondly, you need information that helps you operationalize your study. Operationalization is the process of taking the general idea of your research question and creating an actionable plan that allows an experiment to answer the question. If your study includes statistical analysis, you'll need to determine how other studies have used statistics to answer similar questions.

With that in mind, determine the following:

- What data did similar studies collect? Which variables?
- How did they measure the variables?
- How did they draw their sample?
- What methods did they use to analyze the data? Which analyses and experimental designs?

You'll also want to learn about the strengths, weaknesses, and mistakes that other studies have made. Avoid the mistakes of others and build on their strengths!

The research phase should produce a research question, in-depth knowledge of the subject-area and relevant findings, and a thorough understanding of how other researchers have operationalized similar studies. This background information helps you design your own experiment.

Step 2: Operationalize Your Study

Operationalizing a study is the process of taking your research question, using the background information you gathered, and a formulating an actionable plan. This plan includes everything from defining variables to how you'll analyze the data.

Variables: What Will You Measure?

Studies that use statistics to answer questions require you to collect data in the form of variables that you'll analyze. Consequently, you must define the variables that you will measure and decide how you'll measure them. If you do not collect the correct data or measure it inaccurately, you might not be able to answer your research question. In fact, thanks to confounding variables, the variables you do not measure can impact the results for the variables that you do measure! Take your time determining which variables you'll need to measure to answer your research question.

For example, if you are studying depression, how will you define and measure depression? Your literature review should inform your decision about using an accepted definition for depression and choosing a scientifically validated methodology for assessing depression. Science builds on itself!

If you're trying to predict depression, describe its relationships with other variables, or evaluate treatments, you'll need to define those variables operationally and determine how you'll measure them.

Types of Variables and Treatments

Typically, studies want to understand how changes in one or more variables affect the outcome variable. Depending on the type of experiment, the researchers will either control or not control the variables. If you control the variables, you'll need to decide on the settings for the controllable variables.

Most studies include a treatment, intervention, or some other comparison it wants to make. You'll need to define the treatment and ensure a system is in place to deliver it as required. That's true not only for medical treatments but with any intervention.

For example, I participated in an exercise intervention study to determine whether it affects bone density. We defined our intervention as sessions that occur three times a week and consist of 30 impacts that are six times the subjects' body weights. We had the procedures, equipment, and training in place to ensure our subjects received the intervention as we defined it.

Measurement Methodology: How Will You Take Measurements?

You'll also need to specify how you will take measurements. What equipment will you use? How will you reduce other sources of variation?

Precision and accuracy are essential in research. Ensure that your plan describes how to obtain good measurements. For example, I once wrote a detailed equipment calibration document to ensure high quality measurements over the course of the study. For that study, good measurements depended on daily, standardized calibrations.

Create a Sampling Plan: How Will You Collect Samples for Studying?

Researchers must specify the particular population they're studying. For example, will you include all levels of depression or only mild to severe cases? What ages, socioeconomic statuses, and other factors will define your population.

Perhaps you're studying the strength of products from a manufacturing process. You'll still need to ensure that you obtain a representative sample. You might need to incorporate different manufacturing lines, shifts, and other relevant conditions.

After you define your population, you need to devise a plan for collecting a sample from that population. Your sample contains the people or objects that your study assesses. Studies that use inferential statistics take sample data and draw inferences about a population. However, these studies must gather samples in a manner that produces unbiased estimates. This process often involves random sampling because a convenience method can introduce bias.

Literature reviews often reveal sample collection methodologies other researchers have used in your study area. Determine where and how you'll collect the sample, including the date and time, location, and so on.

Finally, how much data should you collect? On the one hand, you want to collect enough data to have a reasonable chance of detecting a practically significant effect. On the other hand, you don't want to obtain such a large sample that it wastes your time and resources. A statistical power analysis helps you choose a sample size that strikes a balance between these two competing goals. However, to perform a power analysis, you need estimates for effect size and variability in the data. Again, look at your literature review!

Design the Experimental Methods

You'll need to define your hypothesis in a form amenable to statistical analysis and choose the appropriate analysis. Your hypothesis must be testable, which means that the data you collect will either support or reject the hypothesis. Determine the statistical analyses that can adequately test your hypotheses. These methodology decisions start at a very high level, such as choosing between a randomized experiment or an observational study. From there, you can work your way down to more fundamental questions. We'll focus on these designs in the next chapter.

For example, will you compare means, medians, proportions, or rates between groups? Or perhaps assess the relationship between nominal variables or continuous variables? All these issues affect the statistical analyses you can perform.

Additionally, there are the nuts and bolts for each type of analysis that you'll need to decide. What significance level will you use? One-tailed or two-tailed hypothesis tests? If you use ANOVA, will you follow up with a post hoc test? If so, which one? These analytical decisions go beyond the scope of this book, but I cover them in my hypothesis testing book.

Your plan should limit the number of analyses and models you'll use. Each statistical test has an error rate. The more tests you perform, the higher the overall chances of a false result. Making these methodology decisions in advance helps reduce data mining. It prevents you from using multiple techniques and then cherry picking the best results. In this manner, a data analysis plan lowers the probability of false positives caused by running into chance correlations.

The operationalization stage should produce a plan that tells you what you'll measure, how you'll measure it, how you will collect a sample, the size of the sample, and how you'll analyze the data.

Step 3: Data Collection

At this point, you've operationalized your study and have a plan of action. After you make the necessary arrangements, you should be ready to collect data! Depending on the nature of your research, this can be quite a long process. Whether you're in the lab measuring, out administering surveys in the field, or working with human subjects, data collection is often the portion of the study that takes the most time and work. Hurray! You're doing science!

Often, you'll need to set up the proper conditions to take measurements and verify that everything is working correctly. Perhaps you need to get the lab conditions just right and ensure the equipment is functioning properly to obtain valid measurements. Or, you're going through a detailed process to obtain a truly random sample. Sometimes it is difficult to recruit a sufficient number of human subjects. The procedures might also involve training other personnel to perform tasks precisely as prescribed. I once had to create a training video to obtain consistent results!

While you're generally working from your operational plan, it's not uncommon to encounter surprises, and you'll need to adapt. Hopefully, your subject-area knowledge and literature review help you anticipate most surprises, but the thing about science is that you're often studying something that researchers haven't fully studied before. Expect surprises!

Step 4: Statistical Analysis

Like the data collection stage of your study, you should already have the analysis phase defined. If you're "winging it," you're not doing it right! In a nutshell, be sure that you're analyzing the data correctly, satisfying the assumptions where necessary, and drawing the proper conclusions.

However, there is a vital point to make here. Problems anywhere in this process can prevent you from making discoveries or invalidate the findings well before you even get to the statistical analysis. As the old saying goes, garbage in, garbage out. If you put garbage data into the statistical analysis, it'll spit out garbage results. If all the steps leading up to your analysis are not carefully thought out and performed, you might not be able to trust the results or miss important findings. Science is all about getting all the details correct.

Step 5: Writing the Results

After you collect the data and analyze it, you need to write up the results to inform other researchers about what you've found. Indicate which hypotheses the data support, the overall conclusions, and what they represent in the framework of the scientific field or real-world setting. However, it involves more than just writing up the findings.

The scientific method works by replicating results—or the failure to do so. The scientific process tends to cause the correct answers for research questions to rise the top over time through successful replication. Conversely, it weeds out incorrect results after they fail to replicate.

Consequently, you'll need to provide enough information about how you conducted your study so other researchers can repeat it and, hopefully, replicate the results. Typically, you'll include aspects of the first four steps (background research, operationalization, data collection, and analysis) in the final write up. The standards vary by field, so you should see how studies in your area document themselves. In this manner, your research becomes part of the knowledgebase for future studies to build on—just like you did during your literature review! Additionally, all the details help other researchers determine the strengths and weaknesses of your study so they can interpret the results while understanding the context.

Summary and Next Steps

This chapter provides an overview of how statistical analyses fits into the scientific process. Statistical analysis is a crucial step in the scientific process because it objectively tells you which hypothesis the data favor. However, there is a long list of items before the statistical analysis that must all proceed correctly for you to be able to trust the results.

The next chapter focuses on designing experiments and the different options that are available. Researchers design experiments to make discoveries and test hypotheses.

CHAPTER 7

Experimental Methods

Throughout this book, you've learned about the different types of data, the different types of relationships that can exist between variables, and how to graph and identify these relationships. All of that information is at the core of how we can use numbers to learn. For instance, you can compare groups to see how they differ by central tendencies and variability.

Then, you learned about using inferential statistics to learn about a population, along with the need to use a sampling methodology that produces a representative sample.

After that, we looked at the broad picture of the scientific process and saw how statistical analyses fit into it. Now, we'll zoom in on that process and take a look at experimental methods, which is how we use numbers, statistics, and analyses to expand the frontiers of human knowledge.

An experiment is a procedure to make a discovery or test a hypothesis. To conduct an experiment, researchers manipulate, measure, and control variables. Typically, the goal is to establish a causal relationship between variables. Researchers want to influence, predict, and explain outcomes. Experiments push back the boundaries of science by creating new knowledge. They can improve lives by creating knowledge that enhances products, services, methods, or just by increasing the overall understanding of how things work in the world.

For experiments to create new knowledge, scientists use designs that include procedures and variables that allow them to identify relationships that answer their research questions. For example, they might want to investigate the effectiveness of a new vaccine by comparing infection rates in vaccinated and unvaccinated groups. They must ensure that their experimental design allows them to pinpoint the cause to the variables, treatments, and processes that they are testing while ruling out other possible explanations. They also want to be sure that the effect they observe doesn't exist only in their small sample but also exists in a larger population.

The term experiment covers many different types of design. The strictest definition of an experiment is known as a true experiment. In a true experiment, the researchers randomly select subjects from the population, randomly assign subjects to the treatment groups, and control the treatments and all relevant conditions they experience in a lab setting.

However, there are broader definitions of experiments. These definitions include quasi-experimental designs that don't use representative samples or random assignment. Researchers might not even control the treatments and other conditions that the subjects experience.

How people within a field think about experiments depends on the area.

Physical sciences, such as chemistry and physics, frequently perform true, randomized experiments. Researchers in these areas can complete their investigations in labs where they can control experimental samples and conditions more easily than researchers in social sciences.

In the social sciences, it's more difficult, or even impossible, to randomly assign subjects and control the treatments and other variables. Experimenting in a lab is often not possible. Consequently, areas such as psychology and sociology often use quasi-experiments, such as observational studies.

Physical objects are easier to randomize and control in a lab. People are much more difficult!

There are many different types of experimental designs. Statisticians have written entire textbooks about the various processes. In this introductory book, I'll cover two broad types of experimental designs—true experiments and quasi-experiments. Fundamentally, these two approaches are dramatically different, but they have the same ultimate goals and similar challenges.

Types of Variables in Experiments

Let's define the two fundamental types of variables that you'll include in your experiment.

Dependent Variables

The dependent variable is a variable in the experiment that you want to explain or predict. The values of this variable *depend* on other variables. It's also known as the response variable, outcome variable, and it is commonly denoted using a Y. Traditionally, analysts graph dependent variables on the vertical, or Y, axis. Frequently, you'll compare the outcome variable between groups to estimate the effect size of your treatment, intervention, or process.

Independent Variables

Independent variables are the variables that you include in the experiment to explain or predict changes in the dependent variable. In true experiments, independent variables are systematically set and changed by the researchers. However, in observational studies, the values of the independent variables are not set by researchers but observed instead. These variables are also known as predictor variables, input variables, experimental factors, and are commonly denoted using Xs. On graphs, analysts place independent variables on the horizontal, or X, axis.

For example, in a vaccination study, the infection rate is the dependent variable. That's the outcome we measure. The independent variable is a categorical grouping variable that defines the treatment and control group. In this experiment, we'll control who receives vaccination treatment. To estimate the effectiveness of the vaccines, we compare the infection rates between the treatment and control groups.

Causation versus Correlation

Before getting into the experimental methods themselves, we need to look at a potential problem that all experiments face. When you conduct an experiment, you typically want to identify causal relationships. Does event A cause outcome B? However, determining that an event causes an outcome, rather than merely being correlated, requires your experiment to include design elements that control or rule out other possible explanations.

Causation indicates that an event affects an outcome. Do fatty diets cause heart problems? If you study for a test, does it cause you to get a higher score?

You'll read a lot about confounding variables and how to manage them. All the experimental designs we cover have different methods for addressing confounders because it is such a critical issue. To get started on that topic, we need to revisit the old chestnut about correlation versus causation!

The expression is, "correlation does not imply causation." Consequently, you might think that it applies to things like Pearson's correlation coefficient. And, it does apply to that statistic. However, we're really talking about relationships between variables in a broader context. Pearson's is for two continuous variables. However, a relationship can involve different types of variables such as categorical variables, counts, binary data, and so on.

For example, in a medical experiment, you might have a categorical variable that defines which treatment group subjects belong to—a control group and several different treatment groups. If the health outcome is a continuous variable, you can assess the differences between group means. If the means differ by group, then you can say that mean health outcomes depend on the treatment group. There's a correlation, or relationship, between the type of treatment and health outcome. Or, perhaps the outcome is binary, say infected and not infected. In that case, we'd compare group proportions of the infected/not infected between groups to determine whether treatment correlates with infection rates.

Throughout this section, I'll refer to correlation and relationships in this broader sense—not just literal correlation coefficients. But rather relationships between variables, such as differences between group means and proportions, regression coefficients, associations between pairs of categorical variables, and so on.

In statistics, causation is a bit tricky. Correlation doesn't necessarily imply causation. An association or correlation between variables indicates that the values vary together. It does not necessarily suggest that changes in one variable cause changes in the other variable. Proving causality can be difficult.

If correlation does not prove causation, what statistical test do you use to assess causality? That's a trick question because no statistical analysis can make that determination. In this section, learn about why you want to determine causation and how to do that.

Confounding Variables

As a critical component of the scientific method, experiments typically set up contrasts between a control group and one or more treatment groups. The idea is to determine whether the effect, which is often the difference between a treatment group and the control group, is statistically significant. If the effect is significant, group assignment correlates with different outcomes.

However, as you have read, correlation does not necessarily imply causation. In other words, the experimental groups can have different mean outcomes, but the treatment might not be causing those differences even when the differences are statistically significant.

The difficulty in establishing causality is the potential existence of confounding variables or confounders. As you read about in chapter 3, confounders are alternative explanations for differences between the experimental groups. Remember the spurious correlation between ice cream sales and shark attacks?

Confounding variables correlate with both the experimental groups and the outcome variable. In this situation, confounding variables can be the actual cause for the outcome differences rather than the treatments themselves. As you'll see, if an experiment does not account for confounding variables, they can bias the results and make them untrustworthy.

Example of Confounding in an Experiment

An example will help clarify how confounding can obscure your results. Suppose we want to determine whether regular vitamin consumption improves health outcomes. To keep things simple, we have the following two experimental groups:

- Control group: Does not consume vitamin supplements
- Treatment group: Regularly consumes vitamin supplements.

In this experiment, we measure a specific health outcome. After the experiment is complete, we perform a hypothesis test to determine whether the mean outcomes for these two groups are different. Assume the test results indicate that the mean outcome in the treatment group is significantly better than the control group.

Why can't we assume that the vitamins improved the health outcomes? After all, only the treatment group took the vitamins.

Answering that question depends on how we assigned the subjects to the experimental groups. If we let the subjects decide which group to join based on their existing vitamin habits, it opens the door to confounding variables. It's reasonable to assume that people who take vitamins regularly also tend to have other healthy habits. These habits are confounders because they correlate with both vitamin consumption and the health outcome measure.

In fact, studies have found that supplement users are more physically active, have healthier diets, have lower blood pressure, and so on compared to those who don't take supplements. If subjects who already take vitamins regularly join the treatment group voluntarily, they bring these healthy habits disproportionately to the treatment group. Consequently, these habits will be much more prevalent in the treatment group than the control group.

The healthy habits are the confounding variables—the potential alternative explanations for the difference in our study's health outcome. These systematic differences between groups at the start of the study might cause the difference in the health outcome at the end of the study—and not the vitamin consumption itself!

If our experiment doesn't account for these confounding variables, we can't trust the results. While we obtained differences in health outcomes, we don't know for sure whether the vitamins, the systematic differences in habits, or some combination of the two caused the improvements.

Why Determining Causality Is Important

What is the big deal in the difference between correlation and causation? For example, if you observe that as one variable increases, the other variable also tends to increase—isn't that good enough? After all, you've quantified the relationship and learned something about how they behave together.

If you're only predicting events, not trying to understand why they happen, and do not want to alter the outcomes, correlation can be perfectly fine. For example, ice cream sales correlate with shark attacks. If you just need to predict the number of shark attacks, ice cream sales might be a good thing to measure even though it's not causing the shark attacks.

However, if you want to reduce the number of attacks, you'll need to find something that genuinely causes a change in the attacks. As far as I know, sharks don't like ice cream!

There are many occasions where you want to affect the outcome. For example, you might want to do the following:

- Improve health by using medicine, exercising, or flu vaccinations.
- Reducing the risk of adverse outcomes, such as procedures for reducing manufacturing defects.
- Improving outcomes, such as studying for a test.

For intentional changes in one variable to affect the outcome variable, there must be a causal relationship between the variables. After all, if studying does not cause an increase in test scores, there's no point for studying. If the medicine doesn't cause an improvement in your health or ward off disease, there's no reason to take it.

Before you can state that some course of action will improve your outcomes, you must be sure that a causal relationship exists between your variables.

Causation and Hypothesis Tests

Let's take a moment to reflect on why statistically significant hypothesis test results do not signify causation.

Hypothesis tests are inferential procedures. They allow you to use relatively small samples to draw conclusions about entire populations. For the topic of causation, we need to understand what statistical significance means.

Use a hypothesis test to determine whether your data provide sufficient evidence to conclude that a relationship in your sample exists in the population. Tests exist for correlation coefficients, differences between group means, and regression coefficients among many other relationships. You might observe a relationship in your sample, but you need to know whether it exists in the population. Random sampling error (i.e., the luck of the draw) might have created the appearance of a "relationship" in your sample.

Statistical significance indicates that you have sufficient evidence to conclude that the relationship you observe in the sample also exists in the population.

That's it. It doesn't address causality at all.

There's a critical separation between significance and causality:

- Statistical procedures indicate whether you have sufficient evidence to conclude that a sample effect exists in the population.
- Experimental designs determine how confidently you can assume that a treatment causes the effect.

How do experiments determine that a relationship is causal?

In short, to have a chance at asserting that a relationship is causal, your study must have a design that helps rule out other explanations for the association. Scientific studies commonly use the following two methods to handle confounders:

- Use random assignment in a true experiment to reduce the likelihood that systematic differences exist between experimental groups when the investigation begins.
- Statistically control for them in quasi-experiments and observational studies.

I'll cover quasi-experiments and observational studies later in this chapter. For now, let's take a look at how random assignment works in an experimental design.

True Randomized Experiments

To classify as a true experiment, the researchers must do the following:

- Uses a representative sample of the population under study.
- Randomly assign subjects to the experimental groups.
- Have a control group.
- Control the treatment or process that they are testing.

True experiments are the best way to identify causal relationships. These studies often occur in lab settings that control other sources of variation effectively. This stringent design is frequently more expensive and harder to implement than the less strict forms we'll discuss later.

Random assignment uses chance to assign subjects to the control and treatment groups in an experiment. This process helps ensure that the groups are equivalent at the beginning of the study. Having comparable groups increases your confidence that the treatments caused the differences between groups at the end of the study.

Additionally, researchers must be able to control the treatment or process that each group experiences and control other sources of variation. True experiments typically have a control group that serves as a baseline to compare to the outcomes of the treatment groups. If the infection rate for a vaccine is 10%, you don't know if that's an improvement unless you can compare it to an unvaccinated control group.

Random assignment is the magic ingredient that gives true experiments powerful abilities to detect causal relationships. Let's see how that works!

Random Assignment

Note that random assignment is different than random sampling. Random sampling is a process for obtaining a sample that accurately represents a population.

Random assignment uses a chance process to assign subjects to experimental groups. Using random assignment requires that the experimenters can control the group assignment for all study subjects. To illustrate how this works, let's return to our vitamin supplement study. For our research, we must be able to assign our participants to either the control group or the supplement group. Obviously, if we can't assign subjects to the groups, we can't use random assignment!

Additionally, the process must have an equal probability of assigning a subject to any of the groups. For example, in our vitamin supplement study, we can use a coin toss to assign each person to either the control group or supplement group. For more complex experimental designs, we can use a random number generator or even draw names out of a hat.

The random assignment process distributes confounding properties amongst your experimental groups equally. In other words, randomness helps eliminate systematic differences between groups. For our study, flipping the coin tends to equalize the distribution of subjects with healthier habits between the control and treatment group. Consequently, these two groups should start roughly equal for all confounding variables, including healthy habits!

When a study ends, we compare outcomes between groups to see if there are differences. For example, we might use a hypothesis test to determine whether the differences between groups means are statistically significant.

Random assignment is a simple, elegant solution to a complex problem. For any given study area, there can be a long list of confounding variables to worry about. However, using random assignment, you don't need to know what they are, how to detect them, or even measure them. Instead, use random assignment to equalize them across your experimental groups so they're not a problem.

Because random assignment helps ensure that the groups are comparable when the experiment begins, you can be more confident that the treatments caused the post-study differences.

Comparing the Vitamin Study With and Without Random Assignment

Let's compare two scenarios involving our hypothetical vitamin study. Assume that it obtains statistically significant results in both cases.

Scenario 1: We don't use random assignment and, unbeknownst to us, subjects with healthier habits disproportionately end up in the supplement treatment group. The experimental groups differ by both healthy habits and vitamin consumption. Consequently, we can't determine whether it was the habits or vitamins that improved the outcomes.

Scenario 2: We use random assignment and, consequently, the treatment and control groups start with roughly equal levels of healthy habits. The intentional introduction of vitamin supplements in the treatment group is the primary difference between the groups. Consequently, we can more confidently assert that the supplements caused an improvement in health outcomes.

For both scenarios, the statistical results could be identical. However, the methodology behind the second scenario makes a stronger case for a causal relationship between vitamin supplement consumption and health outcomes.

How important is it to use the correct methodology? If the relationship between vitamins and health outcomes is not causal, then consuming vitamins won't *cause* your health outcomes to improve regardless of the results. Instead, it's probably all the other healthy habits!

Let's take a look at a real experiment that used random assignment along with a "blinding" design to help rule out confounders.

Flu Vaccination Experiment

The Monto et al. study is a randomized experiment that evaluates flu vaccinations during the 2007-2008 flu season. (Monto, et al., 2009) Participants are 18-49 years old and healthy. The study follows them from January to April. Researchers drew a random sample from this population. For those who agreed to participate, the researchers randomly assigned them to the vaccination group or control group. We'd expect the random assignment to equalize other characteristics that can influence infection rates between the two groups.

For this experiment, the control group received a placebo, which was a fake shot. Neither the subjects nor the researchers who worked with them know their group assignment. This double-blind design helps prevent researcher and participant expectations from affecting the outcome. These expectations are potential confounders.

Flu shots contain vaccine for three or four strains of the influenza virus that scientists predict will be the most common strains in a flu season. However, there are many other viruses (other strains of flu and non-flu) that can make you sick. Some of these are flu-*like* illnesses that are not the flu but can make you feel like you have the flu.

Consequently, the best flu vaccination studies use a lab to identify the specific viruses that makes their subjects sick. These studies count participants as being infected with the flu only when they catch an influenza strain in the vaccine. Flu shot effectiveness is the reduction in cases involving these particular strains among those who were vaccinated compared to those who were not.

The table below displays the counts of infections by group. I've included the percentages to facilitate comparison.

Group	Flu count	Group size
Vaccinated	28 (3.4%)	813
Placebo	35 (10.8%)	325

The vaccinated group had an infection rate of 3.4% compared to 10.8% in the placebo group. The difference, or treatment effect, is a 7.4% reduction in the infection rate. The researchers performed a hypothesis test, which determined that this difference is statistically significant. In other words, the study provides sufficient evidence to conclude that this effect exists in the population. The confidence interval for this estimate is 3.7% to 10.9%.

Because we know that this was a randomized experiment, it provides solid evidence that the vaccine caused the reduction in the infection rate.

Drawbacks of Randomized Experiments

Scientists consider randomized experiments to be the best for identifying causal relationships. However, despite being the gold standard, they can have a variety of problems.

Researchers strictly control true experiments. In fact, they might be so controlled that they do not represent real-world conditions. An effect apparent in a highly controlled lab might not occur in real-world situations. This type of experiment can also be relatively expensive to set up due to the lab setting and highly controlled environments.

In the physical sciences, it's easier to control the variability of the relatively few conditions that can affect the outcome. However, in social sciences, there might be so many potential variables researchers cannot control that a true experiment is impossible. Additionally, researchers working with human subjects might worry about the natural tendency for people to behave differently in lab settings.

Random assignment helps reduce the chances of systematic differences between the groups at the start of an experiment and, thereby, mitigates the threats of confounding variables and alternative explanations. However, the process does not always equalize all of the confounding variables. Its random nature tends to eliminate systematic differences, but it doesn't always succeed.

Sometimes random assignment is impossible because the experimenters cannot control the treatment or independent variable. For example, if you want to determine how individuals with and without depression perform on a test, you cannot randomly assign subjects to these groups. The same difficulty occurs when you're studying differences between genders.

In other cases, there might be ethical issues. For example, in a randomized experiment, the researchers would want to withhold treatment for the control group. However, if the treatment is a vital medication, it would be unethical to withhold it.

Other times, random assignment might be possible, but it is very challenging. For example, with vitamin consumption, it's generally thought that if vitamin supplements cause health improvements, it's only after very long-term use. It's hard to enforce random assignment with a strict regimen for usage in one group and non-usage in the other group over the long-run. Or imagine a study about smoking. The researchers would find it challenging to assign subjects to the smoking and non-smoking groups randomly!

Quasi-Experiments

Quasi-experiments are similar to true experiments in their attempt to establish causality, but they do not meet all the requirements of a true experiment. Quasi-experiments can bear a strong resemblance to true experiments. They typically have an outcome/dependent variable, at least one independent variable, and designs that compare treatment groups to a control group.

There are a wide variety of types of quasi-experiments to handle different situations. However, the common characteristic for all quasi-experiments is that they do not use random assignment. In some cases, it is impossible or unethical to assign subjects to treatment groups randomly. Perhaps the researchers cannot assign subjects to the experimental groups. Or, maybe they can assign them to the groups but cannot use a random process. For example, the researchers might need to assign the subjects by alphabetical order, ability, cut-off scores, or some other non-random attribute.

Typically, the researchers do not control all the relevant variables in a quasi-experiment. In fact, they might not control the treatment or intervention itself. Instead, the subjects might choose the treatment groups themselves or be assigned by a non-random process—which might not be under the experimenter's control.

Quasi-experiments often include pre-tests that allow researchers to determine whether there are differences between the experimental groups at the beginning of the experiment that might affect the outcomes. Unlike true experiments, quasi-experimental designs often require the researchers to observe and measure confounding variables and then account for them using a statistical model.

Pros and Cons of Quasi-Experiments

True experiments tend to occur in labs where researchers control all conditions, but generalizability to the real world might suffer. On the other hand, quasi-experiments frequently occur in more natural settings outside of the lab. Consequently, statisticians refer to this type of experiment as a natural experiment. Subjects are in their natural environments and often making their own decisions about the treatments and other factors that are relevant to the researcher's outcome variable. Consequently, generalizability to the real-world is less of a concern for quasi-experiments.

However, moving away from random assignment increases questions about causality. Differences in outcomes might be attributable to confounding variables and alternative explanations rather than the treatment itself.

As the previous section explained, true experiments are typically more expensive and complicated to set up. Consequently, limited resources can prevent researchers from conducting a true experiment, but they might be able to afford a less stringent design.

In cases where random assignment is impossible or unethical, true experiments are not an option. The standard examples for when to use quasi-experiments are for situations where random assignment is not possible, such as educational interventions, public policy changes, and large-scale health interventions. You simply can't assign subjects randomly or even test them in a lab!

Next, we'll look much more deeply into observational studies. These are a type of quasi-experiment that you use when you can't assign subjects to the groups randomly, and you do not control the treatment or intervention. The researchers simply observe. It's the very definition of a natural experiment. Observational studies reduce the problem of confounding variables by incorporating confounders into a statistical model of the experimental design.

Observational Studies

For a myriad of reasons, researchers might not be able to use random assignment. Observational studies use samples to draw conclusions about a population when the researchers do not control the treatment, or independent variable, that relates to the primary research question.

Previously, I showed how random assignment reduces systematic differences between experimental groups at the beginning of the study. This process increases your confidence that the treatments caused any differences between groups you observe at the end of the study.

Unfortunately, using random assignment is not always possible. For these cases, you can conduct an observational study. In this section, you will learn about observational studies, why these studies must account for confounding variables, and how to do so. Finally, we'll review a published observational study about vitamin supplement usage so you can see how it works.

In observational studies, researchers only observe the subjects and do not interfere or try to influence the outcomes. In other words, the researchers do not control the treatments or assign subjects to experimental groups. Instead, they observe and measure variables of interest and look for relationships between them. Usually, researchers conduct observational studies when it is difficult, impossible, or unethical to assign study participants to the experimental groups randomly. If you can't randomly assign subjects, then you observe them in their self-selected states.

Randomized studies are better, and you should usually randomize whenever possible. However, if randomization is not possible, science should not come to a halt. After all, we still want to learn things, discover relationships, and make discoveries. For these cases, observational studies are a good alternative.

When to Use Observational Studies

Let's start by looking at cases where random assignment is problematic. Despite that constraint, we can still conduct observational studies and draw conclusions about effects.

If you're studying how depression affects the performance of an activity, it's impossible to assign subjects to the depression and control group randomly. However, you can have subjects with and without depression perform the activity and compare the results.

Or, imagine trying to assign subjects to cigarette smoking and non-smoking groups randomly?! However, you can observe people in both groups and assess the differences in health outcomes.

Suppose you're studying a treatment for a disease. Ideally, you recruit a group of patients who all have the disease, and then randomly assign them to the treatment and control group. However, it's unethical to withhold the treatment, which rules out a control group. Instead, you can compare patients who voluntarily do not use the medicine to those who do use it.

We'll examine an observational study about vitamin supplement consumption and how that affects the risk of death. For this experiment, you can conceivably design an experiment that uses random assignment to place each subject in either the vitamin treatment group or the control group. However, the study we'll look at assesses vitamin consumption in 40,000 participants over two decades. It's unrealistic to enforce the treatment and control protocols over such a long time for so many people!

In all these examples, the researchers do not assign subjects to the experimental groups. Instead, they observe people who are already in these groups and compare the outcomes.

Accounting for Confounders in Observational Studies

While observational studies get around the inability to assign subjects randomly, as you saw earlier, the lack of random assignment opens the door to the problem of confounding variables. Because there is no random process that equalizes experimental groups in observational studies, confounding variables can systematically differ between groups when the investigation begins. Consequently, confounders can be the actual cause for differences in outcome at the end of the study rather than the primary variable of interest. If an experiment does not account for confounding variables, confounders can bias the results and make them untrustworthy.

Despite the limitations, observational studies can be a valid approach. However, you must ensure that your design accounts for confounding variables. Fortunately, there are several methods for doing just that!

In the section about random assignment, I describe that process as an elegant solution for confounding variables. You don't need to measure or even know which variables are confounders, and randomization will still mitigate their effects.

On the other hand, observational studies don't use random assignment and confounders can be distributed disproportionately. Consequently, experimenters need to know which variables are confounders, measure them, and then use a method to account for them. It involves more work, and the additional measurements can increase the costs. And there's always a chance that researchers will fail to identify a confounder, not account for it, and produce biased results. However, if randomization isn't an option, consider an observational study.

Trait matching and statistically controlling confounders using multivariate procedures are two standard approaches for incorporating confounding variables.

Matching

Matching is a technique that involves selecting study participants who have similar characteristics overall and differ mainly by the variable of interest or treatment. Rather than using random assignment to equalize the experimental groups, the experimenters do it by matching observable characteristics. The researchers use subject-area knowledge to identify characteristics that are critical to match. For every participant in the treatment group, the researchers find a participant with comparable traits to include in the control group. Matching facilitates valid comparisons between similar groups.

For example, a vitamin supplement study using matching will select subjects who have similar health-related habits and attributes. The goal is that vitamin consumption will be the primary difference between the groups, which helps you attribute differences in health outcomes to vitamin consumption. However, the researchers are still observing participants who decide whether they consume supplements.

Matching has some drawbacks. The experimenters might not be aware of all the relevant characteristics they need to match. In other words, the groups might be different in an essential aspect that the researchers don't recognize. For example, in the hypothetical vitamin study, there might be a healthy habit or attribute that affects the outcome that the researchers don't measure and match. These unmatched characteristics might cause the observed differences in outcomes rather than vitamin consumption.

Multiple Regression

Random assignment and matching use different methods to equalize the experimental groups. However, statistical techniques, such as multiple regression analysis, don't try to balance the groups but instead use a model that accounts for confounding variables. These studies statistically control for confounding variables.

In multiple regression analysis, including a variable in the model holds it constant while the treatment variable fluctuates. This process allows you to isolate the role of the treatment while accounting for confounders.

As with matching, the challenge is to identify, measure, and include all confounders in the regression model. Failure to include a confounding variable in a regression model can bias your results.

Next, we'll look at a published study that uses multiple regression to account for confounding variables.

Multiple regression goes beyond the scope of this book. For more information, read my book: *Regression Analysis: An Intuitive Guide.*

Vitamin Supplement Observational Study

Mursu et al. use a longitudinal observational study that ran 22 years to evaluate differences in death rates for subjects who used vitamin supplements regularly compared to those who did not use them (Mursu, 2011). This study used surveys to record the characteristics of approximately 40,000 participants. The surveys asked questions about potential confounding variables such as demographic information, food intake, health details, physical activity, and, of course, supplement intake.

Because this is an observational study, the subjects decided for themselves whether they were taking vitamin supplements. Consequently, it's safe to assume that supplement users and non-users might be different in other ways. From their article, the researchers found the following pre-existing differences between the two groups:

"Supplement users had a lower prevalence of diabetes mellitus, high blood pressure, and smoking status; a lower BMI and waist to hip ratio, and were less likely to live on a farm. Supplement users had a higher educational level, were more physically active, and were more likely to use estrogen replacement therapy. Also, supplement users were more likely to have a lower intake of energy, total fat, and monounsaturated fatty acids, saturated fatty acids and to have a higher intake of protein, carbohydrates, polyunsaturated fatty acids, alcohol, whole grain products, fruits, and vegetables."

Whew! That's a long list of differences! Supplement users were different from non-users in a multitude of ways that are likely to affect their risk of dying. The researchers must account for these confounding variables when they compare supplement users to non-users. If they do not, their results can be biased.

Using Multiple Regression to Statistically Control for Confounders

To account for these initial differences, the researchers use regression analysis and include the confounding variables in the model.

The researchers present three regression models. The simplest model accounts only for age and caloric intake. Next, are two models that include additional confounding variables beyond age and calories. The first model adds various demographic information and seven health measures. The second model includes everything in the previous model and adds several more specific dietary intake measures. Using statistical significance as a guide for specifying the correct regression model, the researchers present the model with the most variables as the basis for their final results.

It's instructive to compare the raw results and the final regression results.

Raw results

The raw differences in death risks for consumers of folic acid, vitamin B6, magnesium, zinc, copper, and multivitamins are NOT statistically significant. However, the raw results show a reduction in the death risk for users of B complex, C, calcium, D, and E.

However, these raw results do not control for the long list of differences between groups. After using the regression model to control for the confounding variables statistically, the results change dramatically.

Adjusted results

Of the 15 supplements that the study tracked, researchers found consuming seven of these supplements were linked to a statistically significant INCREASE in death risk (p-value < 0.05): multivitamins (increase in death risk 2.4%), vitamin B6 (4.1%), iron (3.9%), folic acid (5.9%), zinc (3.0%), magnesium (3.6%), and copper (18.0%). Only calcium was associated with a statistically significant reduction in death risk of 3.8%.

In short, the raw results suggest that those who consume supplements either have the same or lower death risks than non-consumers. However, these results do not account for the multitude of healthier habits and attributes in the group that uses supplements.

In fact, these confounders seem to produce most of the apparent benefits in the raw results because, after you statistically control the effects of these confounding variables, the results worsen for those who consume vitamin supplements. The adjusted results indicate that most vitamin supplements actually increase your death risk!

This study illustrates how confounders biased the raw results to make vitamin consumption outcomes look better than they are.

In conclusion, if you can't randomly assign subjects to the experimental groups, an observational study might be right for you. However, be aware that you'll need to identify, measure, and account for confounding variables in your experimental design.

CHAPTER 8

Evaluating Experiments

You learned the basics about experimental designs and the different ways they strive to identify causal relationships. This chapter provides you with criteria to evaluate experiments, whether it's your experiment or one performed by someone else.

These criteria include the nitty-gritty details, such as what instrument did you use to measure an item. And they extend to thought exercises that force you to step back and look at an experiment in a broader context. Collectively, these criteria help you determine whether experimental results depict what the analysts think they do.

The issue we'll start with is causation. Yes, we covered it thoroughly from the angle of designing experiments. However, there are different ways of thinking about causality in a broader context rather than just from the relatively narrow standpoint of a single study.

Then, we'll move on to determining whether experimental data qualifies as "good data." Good data are reliable and valid. These two concepts have special meanings in a statistical context. If you don't have reliable and valid data, you can't draw sound conclusions.

When the data are reliable and valid, you need to evaluate the validity of the study itself using different criteria. If you have good data but do not have experimental validity, you still can't draw reasonable conclusions. Assessing experiments is a multilayered process!

Hill's Criteria of Causation

Determining whether a causal relationship exists requires far more in-depth subject area knowledge and contextual information than you can include in a hypothesis test or a single experiment. In 1965, Austin Hill, a medical statistician, tackled this question in a paper that's become the standard (Hill, A., 1965). While he introduced it in the context of epidemiological research, you can apply his ideas to other fields.

Hill describes nine criteria to help establish causal connections. The goal is to satisfy as many criteria as possible. No single guideline is sufficient. However, it's often impossible to meet all the criteria. These guidelines are an exercise in critical thought. They show you how to think about determining causation and highlight essential qualities to consider.

Strength

A strong, statistically significant relationship is more likely to be causal. The idea is that causal relationships are likely to produce statistical significance. If you have significant results, at the very least you have reason to believe that the association in your sample also exists in the population—which is a good thing. After all, if the relationship only appears in your sample, you don't have anything meaningful! Correlation still does not imply causation, but a statistically significant relationship is a good starting point.

However, there are many more criteria to satisfy! There's a critical caveat for this criterion as well. Confounding variables can mask a correlation that actually exists. They can also create the appearance of correlation where causation doesn't exist, as shown with the ice cream and shark attack example. A significant relationship is simply a hint.

Consistency

When there is a real, causal connection, the result should be repeatable. Other experimenters in other locations ought to be able to reproduce the results. It's not one and done. Replication builds up confidence that the relationship is causal. Preferably, the replication efforts use other methods, researchers, and locations.

Specificity

It's easier to determine that a relationship is causal if you can rule out other explanations. I write about ruling out other reasons in the sections about randomized experiments and observational studies. In a more general sense, it's essential to study the literature, consider other plausible hypotheses, and, hopefully, be able to rule them out or otherwise control for them. You need to be sure that what you're studying is causing the observed change rather than something else of which you're unaware.

It's important to note that you don't need to prove that your variable of interest is the only factor that affects the outcome. For example, smoking causes lung cancer, but it's not the only thing that causes it. However, you do need to perform experiments that account for other relevant factors and be able to attribute some causation to your variable of interest specifically.

Temporality

Causes should precede effects. Ensure that what you consider to be the cause occurs before the effect. Sometimes it can be challenging to determine which way causality runs. Hill uses the following example. A particular diet might lead to an abdominal disease. However, it's also possible that the disease leads to specific dietary habits.

Biological Gradient

Hill was a biologist, hence the focus on biological questions. He suggests that for a genuinely causal relationship, there should be a dose-response type of relationship. If a little bit of exposure causes a little bit of change, a larger exposure should cause more change. Hill uses cigarette smoking and lung cancer as an example—smoking more frequently corresponds with a greater risk of lung cancer. You can apply the same type of thinking in other fields. Does more studying lead to even higher scores?

However, be aware that the relationship might not remain linear. As the dose increases beyond a threshold, the response can taper off.

Plausibility

If you can find a plausible mechanism that explains the causal nature of the relationship, it supports the notion of a causal relationship. For example, biologists understand how antibiotics inhibit microbes on a biological level.

However, Hill points out that you should be careful because there are limits to scientific knowledge at any given moment. A causal mechanism might not be known at the time of the study even if one exists. Consequently, Hill says, "we should not demand" that a study meets this requirement.

Coherence

The probability that a relationship is causal is higher when it is consistent with related causal relationships that are generally known and accepted as facts. If your results outright disagree with accepted facts, it's more likely to be correlation. Assess causality in the broader context of related theory and knowledge.

Experiment

Randomized experiments are the best way to identify causal relationships. Experimenters control the treatment (or factors involved), randomly assign the subjects, and help manage other sources of variation. Hill calls satisfying this criterion the most reliable support for causation. However, randomized experiments are not always possible as I write about in my post about observational studies.

Analogy

If there is an accepted, causal relationship that is similar to one in your research, it supports causation for the current study. Hill writes, "With the effects of thalidomide and rubella before us we would surely be ready to accept slighter but similar evidence with another drug or another viral disease in pregnancy."

Determining whether a correlation represents causation requires much deliberation. Properly designing experiments and using statistical procedures can help you make that determination. But there are many other factors to consider.

Use your critical thinking and subject-area expertise to think about the big picture. If there is a causal relationship, you'd expect to see replication with consistent results, other causes ruled out, results that fit with established theory, a plausible mechanism, and the cause precedes the effect.

Properties of Good Data

Measuring a person or item involves assigning scores to represent an attribute. This process creates the data that we analyze. However, to provide meaningful results, that data must be good. And, not all data are good!

How do researchers assess data quality? Typically, researchers need to collect data using an instrument and evaluate the quality of measurements. In other words, they conduct a study before the main study.

For data to be good enough to use in inferential statistics, they must be reliable and valid.

Reliability

Reliability refers to the consistency of the measure. Reliable measures are reproducible. High reliability indicates that the measurement system produces similar results under the same conditions. If you measure the same item or person multiple times, you want to obtain comparable values.

If you take measurements multiple times and obtain very different values, your data are not reliable. Numbers are meaningless if repeated measures do not produce similar values. What's the correct value? No one knows! This inconsistency hampers your ability to draw conclusions and understand relationships.

Suppose you have a bathroom scale that displays very inconsistent results from one time to the next. It would be hard to use your scale to determine your correct weight and to know whether you are losing weight.

Inadequate data collection procedures and low quality or defective data collection tools can produce unreliable data. Additionally, some characteristics are more challenging to measure. For example, the length of an object is concrete. On the other hand, a psychological construct, such as conscientiousness, can be trickier to measure reliably.

When assessing studies, evaluate data collection methodologies and consider whether any issues undermine their reliability.

Analysts assess three types of reliability—test-retest, internal, and inter-rater reliability. Typically, appraising these forms of reliability involves taking multiple measures of the same person, object, or construct and assessing scatterplots and correlations of the measurements. Reliable measurements have high correlations because the scores are similar.

Test-Retest Reliability

Analysts often assume that measurements should be consistent across a short time period. If you measure your height twice over a couple of days, you should obtain roughly the same measurements.

To assess test-retest reliability, the experimenters typically measure a group of participants on two occasions within a few days. Usually, you'll evaluate the reliability of the repeated measures using scatterplots and correlation coefficients. You expect to see high correlations and tight lines on the scatterplot when the characteristic you are measuring is consistent over a short period and you have a reliable measurement system.

This type of reliability establishes the degree to which a test can produce stable, consistent scores across time. However, in practice, measurement instruments are never entirely consistent.

Keep in mind that some characteristics are not expected to be consistent across time. A good example is your mood, which can change from moment to moment. A test-retest assessment of mood is not likely to produce a high correlation even though it might be a useful measurement instrument.

Internal Reliability

This type of reliability assesses consistency across items within a single instrument. Researchers evaluate internal reliability when they're using instruments such as a survey or personality inventories. In these instruments, multiple items relate to a single construct. Questions that measure the same characteristic should have a high correlation. People who indicate they are risk-takers should also note that they participate in dangerous activities. If items that supposedly measure the same underlying construct have a low correlation, they are not consistent with each other and might not measure the same thing.

Inter-rater reliability

This type of reliability assesses consistency across different observers, judges, or evaluators. When different observers produce similar measurements for the same item or person, there is a high correlation between scores. Inter-rater reliability is essential when subjectivity or skill of the evaluator plays a role. For example, assessing the quality of a writing sample involves subjectivity. Researchers can employ rating guidelines to reduce subjectivity. Comparing the scores from different evaluators for the same writing sample helps establish the reliability of the measure.

Validity

Validity refers to whether the measurements reflect what they're supposed to measure. This concept is a broader issue than reliability. Researchers need to consider whether they're measuring what they think they're measuring. Or, do the measurements reflect something else? Does the instrument measure what it claims to measure? It's a question that addresses the appropriateness of the data rather than whether measurements are repeatable.

To be valid, a measurement must be reliable. After all, if you don't obtain consistent measurements for the same object or person under similar conditions, it can't be valid. If every time you step on your bathroom scale it says something different, it's unreliable and it is also invalid.

Now, suppose you have a reliable measurement. You step on your scale a few times in a short period and it displays very similar weights. It's reliable. But the weight might be incorrect.

Just because you can measure the same object multiple times and get consistent values, it does not necessarily indicate that the measurements reflect the desired characteristic.

Validity is usually less of a concern for tangible measurements like height and weight. You might have a biased bathroom scale if it tends to read too high or too low—but it still measures weight. Validity is often a more significant concern in the social sciences where you can measure intangible constructs such as self-esteem and positive outlook. If you're assessing the psychological construct of conscientiousness, you need to ensure that the measurement instrument asks questions that evaluate this characteristic rather than, say, obedience.

There are many different types of validity. Many refer to the dataset itself, as discussed above, but several other types refer to the conclusions that researchers make from an experiment. Let's take a look at several of the more common types. We'll start with types of data validity and then move on to experimental validity.

Data Validity

Face Validity

Face validity is the simplest and weakest type of validity. Does the measurement instrument appear "on its face" to measure the intended construct? For an instrument that assesses thrill-seeking behavior, you'd expect it to include questions about seeking excitement, getting bored quickly, and about risky behaviors. If the survey contains these types of questions, then "on its face," it seems like the instrument measures the construct that the researchers intend.

While this is a low bar, it's an important issue to consider. Never overlook the obvious. Ensure that you understand the nature of the instrument and how it assesses a construct. Look at the questions. After all, if an instrument can't clear this fundamental requirement, the other types of validity are a moot point. However, when a measure satisfies face validity, understand it is an intuition or a hunch that it feels correct. It's not a statistical assessment. If your instrument passes this low bar, you still have more validation work ahead of you.

Content Validity

Content validity is similar to face validity in that you assess it qualitatively—but it's a more rigorous form of face validity. The process often involves assessing individual questions on a test and asking experts whether each item appraises the characteristics that the instrument is designed to cover. This process compares the test against the researcher's goals and the theoretical properties of the construct. Researchers systematically determine whether each question contributes and that no aspect is overlooked.

For example, if researchers are designing a survey to measure the attitudes and activities of thrill-seekers, they need to determine whether the questions sufficiently cover both of those aspects.

Criterion Validity

Criterion validity relates to the relationships between the variables in your dataset. If your data are valid, you'd expect to observe a particular correlation pattern between the variables. Researchers typically assess criterion validity by correlating different types of data. For whatever you're measuring, you expect it to have particular relationships with other variables.

For example, measures of anxiety should correlate positively with the number of negative thoughts. Anxiety measure might also correlate positively with depression and eating disorders. If we see this pattern of relationships, it supports criterion validity. Our measure for anxiety correlates with other variables as expected.

On the other hand, if we have a measure of thrill-seeking and a measure of sedentariness, we'd expect there to be a negative correlation between them. High thrill-seeking scores should correspond with low sedentary scores. Additionally, thrill-seekers should participate in a higher number of risky activities. If you see that overall pattern, it supports the notion that the data are valid.

Conversely, if you observe a pattern of relationships that goes against what theory and other research suggests, the instrument might not measure the characteristic that the researcher expects. In this case, the correlation pattern casts doubt on criterion validity.

Criterion validity is also known as convergent validity because scores for different measures converge or correspond with each other as theory suggests. You should observe high correlations (either positive or negative).

Discriminant Validity

This type of validity is the opposite of criterion validity. If you have valid data, you expect particular pairs of variables to correlate positively or negatively. However, for other pairs of variables, you expect no relationship.

For example, if self-esteem and locus of control are not related in reality, your measures of them should also not be related. You should observe a low correlation between scores.

Discriminant validity is also known as divergent validity because it relates to how different constructs are differentiated. Low correlations (close to zero) indicate that the values of one variable do not relate to the values of the other variables. The measures are differentiating between different constructs.

Having data that are reliable and valid are both necessary conditions for drawing causal conclusions from experimental results. However, satisfying these conditions are not enough by themselves. As you'll learn about next, you need to assess the validity of the experiment itself.

Experimental Validity

Experimental validity relates to the design of the study. You must have a valid experimental design to be able to draw sound scientific conclusions. Are the conclusions valid?

Regarding reliability, data validity, and experimental validity, keep in mind that these properties build on each other. We saw that for data to be valid, they must start by being reliable and then also satisfy the requirements for being valid. Likewise, for an experiment to be valid, you must start with valid data and also have a valid experimental design. This chain of reliable data, valid data, and a valid experimental design allows you to draw sound conclusions. It takes only one weak link to invalidate experimental results.

Experimental validity has two broad types—internal and external validity. Let's learn more about them!

Internal Validity

Internal validity is the degree of confidence that a causal relationship exists between the treatment and the difference in outcomes. How likely is it that your treatment caused the differences in results that you observe? Are the researcher's conclusions correct? Or, can changes in the outcome be attributed to other causes?

Establishing interval validity involves assessing data collection procedures, the reliability and validity of the data, the experimental design, and even things such as the setting and duration of the experiment. It could involve understanding events and natural processes that occur outside of the investigation. In other words, it's the whole thing. Does the entirety of the experiment allow you to conclude that the treatment causes the differences in outcomes?

Studies that have a high degree of internal validity provide strong evidence of causality. On the other hand, studies with low internal validity provide weak evidence of causality.

Typically, highly controlled experiments that occur in a lab setting, use random assignment, and include a control group have the highest internal validity. Removing these properties, such as moving from the lab to the real world, not being able to randomize, or not having a control group reduces internal validity.

Internal validity relates to causality for a single study. For the study in question, did the treatment cause changes in the outcomes? Internal validity does not address generalizability to other settings, subjects, or populations. It only assesses causality for one study.

In chapter 7, we looked at experimental designs and saw how they account for confounding variables that provide alternative explanations for the experimental results. All the designs we covered use two or more groups, including a control group, and compare the outcomes between groups. For internal validity, we'll start with single group designs and then proceed to multiple group designs. This approach will help you see the benefits of using multiple groups.

Threats to internal validity are types of confounding variables because they provide alternative explanations for changes in outcomes. They are threats because they make us doubt causality. The real reason for the differences in results might be these potential threats.

Single Group Studies

When studies have a single experimental group, researchers typically conduct a pretest to obtain a baseline score, administer a program or intervention, and then perform a posttest. By comparing the pretest and posttest scores, researchers can assess how subjects have changed since the beginning of the experiment. For example, imagine a weight loss program where the researchers measure the subjects' weights at the beginning, conduct the program, and then measure weights at the end. If the intervention causes weight loss, you'd expect to see decreases between the pretest and posttest.

However, there are various threats to attributing a causal connection between the weight loss program and the changes in weights. The following are causality threats for single group studies:

History: An outside event occurred between the pretest and posttest that affected the outcomes. Perhaps a fitness program became popular in town, and many subjects participated. It might be the fitness program that caused the weight loss rather than the weight loss program we're studying.

Maturation: The change between pretest and posttest scores might represent a process that occurs naturally over time. Imagine if instead of a weight loss program, we are studying an educational program. If the posttest scores are higher at the end, we might be observing regular knowledge acquisition rather than the program causing the increase. If it's a natural process, we would have seen the same change even if the subjects did not participate in the experiment.

Testing: The pretest influences outcomes by increasing awareness or sensitivity among test takers. Suppose that the mere fact of weighing the subjects makes them more weight conscious and increases their motivation to lose weight.

Instrumentation: The change between tests is an artifact of a difference between the pretest and posttest assessment instruments rather than an actual change in outcomes. This threat can involve a change in the instrument, different instructions for administering the test, or researchers using different procedures to take measurements. If the scale stops working correctly at some point after the pretest and displays lower weights in the posttest, the subjects' weights appear to decrease.

Mortality: Mortality refers to an experiment's attrition rates amongst its subjects—not necessarily actual deaths! It becomes a problem when subjects with specific characteristics drop out of the study more frequently than other subjects. If these characteristics are associated with changes in the outcome variable, the systematic loss of subjects with these characteristics can bias the posttest results. For example, in an experiment for an educational program, if the more dedicated learners have more extracurricular activities, they might be more likely to drop out of the study. Losing a disproportionate number of dedicated learners can deceptively reduce the apparent effectiveness of an educational program. This threat is higher for studies that have relatively high attrition rates.

Regression: Regression to the mean. If you get an unusual average in the pre-test, the group will tend to regress to the mean in the posttest. Suppose we're assessing an education program and the pretest produces unusually low means. Regression to the mean will tend to cause the posttest to be higher even if the intervention doesn't cause an increase.

Multiple Groups

We covered multiple group experiments in chapter 7. These experiments have a control group that does not receive the treatment or intervention and at least one treatment group. By moving from a single group to two or more groups, experimental designs can avoid many threats to internal validity.

Suppose we are studying an educational program and can randomly assign subjects to a control group and a treatment group. We can be relatively confident that the two groups start with similar characteristics.

Additionally, we can eliminate single group threats to internal validity because we'd expect them to affect both groups. For example, maturation issues, such as the normal development of skills over time, should occur in both the control group and treatment group. Similarly, if the pretest affects the outcomes, it'll affect them for both groups. The same logic applies to the other threats to validity for single groups. To the extent that any of these threats exist, they should be present in both groups. Comparing the treatment to control groups reveals the effect of the educational program that occurs *in addition to* these other possible explanations.

In other words, if a threat occurs across all experimental groups, that threat does not cause the difference in outcomes between groups.

However, for this to all work out as described, the experimental groups must be similar. As you learned in the previous chapter, random assignment helps ensure that the groups start the same. Unfortunately, random assignment isn't always feasible or even possible. Consequently, as you move away from random assignment, selection bias becomes a concern and introduces its own set of threats to internal validity.

Threats to internal validity for designs with multiple groups are variations of the threats for single group designs. Threats for multiple groups often depend on the introduction of selection bias that causes the groups to be different. Selection bias is more likely to occur in observational studies than true experiments.

Let's do a quick run through to see how it works.

History with selection bias: An event affects the two groups differently because the groups themselves are different.

Maturation with selection bias: The normal process occurs differently between the experimental groups because the groups are different.

Testing with selection bias: The pretest affects the groups differently because the groups are different.

Instrumentation with selection bias: Changes in the instrumentation affects the groups differently.

Mortality with selection bias: The groups experience different attrition rates because the groups differ.

In short, when groups differ initially, these threats can affect them differently and change the outcomes.

For some of these threats, the groups might start out being comparable, but these threats can affect them differently for other reasons. For example, with instrumentation, the scale can malfunction when one group is weighted but not the other group. Or, if the groups start out being equivalent, one group might experience a higher attrition rate by chance rather than a pre-existing difference between the groups.

External Validity

External validity relates to the ability to generalize the results of the experiment to other people, places, or times. We talked about this issue in a more limited manner back when we covered inferential statistics. Scientific studies generally do not want findings that apply only to the relatively few subjects who participated in the study. Instead, studies want to be able to use the experimental results and apply them to a larger population.

For example, if you're assessing a new medication or a new educational program, you don't want to know that it's effective for a handful of people. You want to apply those results beyond just the experimental setting and the particular individuals that participated. That's generalizability—and the heart of the matter for external validity.

There are two broad types of external validity—population validity and ecological validity.

Population validity relates to how well the experimental sample represents a population. Sampling methodology addresses this issue. If you use a random sampling technique to obtain a representative sample, it greatly helps you generalize from the sample to the population because they are similar. Population validity requires a sample that reflects the target population.

On the other hand, if the sample does not represent the population, it reduces external validity and you might not be able to generalize from the sample to the population.

Ecological validity relates to the degree of similarity between the experimental setting and the setting to which you want to generalize. The greater the similarity of key characteristics between settings, the more confident you can be that the results will generalize to that other setting. In this context, "key characteristics" are factors that can influence the outcome variable. Ecological validity requires that the methods, materials, and environment in the experiment approximate the relevant real-world setting to which you want to generalize.

Threats to external validity are differences between experimental conditions and the real-world setting. Threats indicate that you might not be able to generalize the experimental results beyond the experiment. You performed your research in a particular context, at a particular time, and with specific people. As you move to different conditions, you lose the ability to generalize. The ability to generalize the results is never guaranteed. This issue is one that you really need to think about. If another researcher conducted a similar study in a different setting, would it obtain the same results?

Overall, to assess the degree of external validity, evaluate the similarities of the following characteristics between the experimental setting and the real-world setting:

- People
- Places
- Times
- Materials
- Methods
- Conditions

In short, the more similar the experimental environment is to another setting, the more likely you can generalize the results to the other setting. For example, if the study involves human subjects, how do their characteristics and relevant demographic information compare to different contexts?

The relevant characteristics we're assessing for similarity vary based on the nature of the experiment. For studies that involve human subjects, the participants might behave differently in a tightly controlled lab setting than in a more natural environment. That reduces the external validity.

On the other hand, if we're studying the strength of new material, we don't need to worry about it behaving differently when researchers observe it in an artificial lab setting! However, we do need to ensure that lab conditions approximate the actual conditions in which the material will be used. For example, the heat, pressure, humidity, and forces that the material experiences in the lab should represent the actual operating conditions for the material in a real-world setting.

There aren't hard and fast rules when it comes to generalizability. Even when the experimental conditions are similar to a different setting, you might not be able to generalize the results for unexpected reasons. Perhaps the pretest interacted with the treatment to produce an effect that would not occur without the pretest? Or, maybe a unique event happened during the experiment that influenced the results. For example, the researchers' behavior can affect the results. Consequently, some experiments use blind designs where the researchers don't know the group assignments for the subjects. This blinding helps prevent researcher expectations from unintentionally influencing the outcome. We saw this type of design in the flu vaccination study.

Similarly, it can be uncertain where you draw the line for when a setting becomes dissimilar enough to rule out generalizability. You'll need to apply subject-area knowledge and critical thinking.

For example, many studies that relate to medical issues, medicine, and vaccination will use a sample of subjects who are healthy overall. The results from these studies might not apply to people with particular diseases or conditions. In a bone density study that I helped run, we excluded subjects with conditions that affected bone growth, such as diabetes. Consequently, our results probably apply only to people without those conditions.

There can be a wide array of conditions to consider. For example, does performing a study with human subjects from rural locations produce different results than if they are from a metropolitan area? It depends on what you're studying!

The following practices can help increase external validity:

- Use random sampling to obtain a representative sample from the population you are studying.
- Understand how your experiment is similar to and different from the setting(s) to which you want to generalize the results. Identify the factors that are particularly relevant to the research question and minimize the difference between experimental conditions and the real-world setting.

- Replicate your study. If you or other researchers replicate your experiment at different times, in various settings, and with different people, you can be more confident about generalizability.

I want to expand on the importance of that last point about replicating studies. We often want to find a definitive study that concretely answers a research question. However, one study *never* completely resolves a research question. Even when researchers have an exquisite experimental design, have reliable and valid data, excellent internal validity, and no reason to doubt external validity, there's still a lingering question. Can other researchers in a different setting replicate those results? You just don't know for sure until someone attempts to replicate it!

Relationship Between Internal & External Validity

There tends to be a negative correlation between internal and external validity in experiments. Experiments that have high internal validity tend to have lower external validity. And, vice versa.

Why does this happen?

To understand the reason, you must think about the experimental conditions that produce high degrees of internal validity and external validity. They're diametrically opposed!

To produce high internal validity, you need a highly controlled environment that minimizes variability in extraneous variables. By controlling the environmental conditions, implementing strict measurement methodologies, using random assignment, and using a standardized treatment, you can effectively rule out alternative explanations for differences in outcomes. That produces a high degree of confidence in causality, which is high internal validity.

However, that artificial lab environment is a far cry from any real-world setting! To have high external validity, you want the experimental conditions to match the real-world setting. Think back to the natural experiments in chapter 7. These observational studies are much more realistic than a lab setting. You experience the full impact of real-world variability! That creates high external validity because the experimental conditions are virtually the real-world setting. However, as we discussed, those types of studies open the door to confounding variables and alternative explanations for differences in outcomes—in other words, lower internal validity!

So, what's the answer?

Replication! Researchers can conduct multiple experiments in different places and use different methodologies—some true experiments in a lab and other observational studies in the field. This point reiterates the importance of replicating studies because no single study is ever enough.

Checklist for Good Experiments

Many things go into a well-designed and well-performed experiment. The following checklist spans the entire contents of the book. Good experiments have the following properties:

1. Has a defined population that is the focus of the investigation.
2. Uses a representative sampling technique to draw a sample from that population.
3. Has a sufficiently large sample to detect effects.
4. Collects good data—reliable, valid, and unbiased.
5. Makes comparisons between control and treatment groups.
6. Controls for confounders using random assignment, statistical modeling, or other techniques.
7. Uses proper inferential statistical methodologies to test results to determine if there is sufficient evidence to conclude that the effect exists in the population—not just the sample.

Review

This chapter covered a chain of linked topics. These topics included criteria for causation, the validity and reliability of your data, and the validity of your experiment. One weak link can hamper your ability to make sound conclusions from experimental results.

Reliability indicates that when you measure the same person or object multiple times under similar conditions, you'll obtain similar measurements. Reliable data are usually a prerequisite for valid data.

Validity indicates that your measurements reflect the characteristic you intend. For example, you're measuring self-esteem rather than something else, such as a positive outlook.

When your data are both reliable and valid, you can start to assess the validity of your experiment. Experimental validity assesses the conclusions that the researchers draw from their experiment.

Internal validity relates to your confidence that an experiment identifies a causal relationship—that the treatment caused the difference in outcomes. Threats to internal validity reduce your assurance that the relationship is causal because they introduce alternative explanations for the differences. In general, the following conditions improve internal validity:

- Multiple group designs are better than single group designs.
- Random assignment is better than other assignment methods.
- Experiments that occur in highly controlled conditions in a lab setting are better than less controlled, real-world environments.

External validity relates to your confidence in the ability to generalize the results from your study to other settings. The greater the similarity between the experimental conditions and the real-world setting, the higher your confidence that you can generalize experimental findings to other groups and settings.

We also noted how internal validity and external validity tend to have a negative correlation.

Finally, replication is crucial! No single experiment conclusively proves anything regardless of its design strengths.

CHAPTER 9

Wrapping Up and Your Next Steps

This book serves as an introduction to statistics. It opens many doors—doors that have more behind them than I can explain in a single book. Let's quickly review what this book covered and highlight potential avenues for further exploration.

I hope I conveyed that the field of statistics contains a wide array of knowledge and methodologies. People outside of statistics tend to think of it as just calculating the numbers, such as the mean or correlation. It does include those types of things.

However, if you want to use samples to learn about a population and identify causal relationships with confidence, you need to have knowledge that goes well beyond just calculating the numbers. You'll need to know how to collect the data, how to design experiments, how to avoid confounding variables, and how to assess the reliability and validity of your results.

Review of What You Learned in this Book

We started by learning about the field of statistics. This field is the science of learning from data.

For data analysis, we started by learning about different types of data and how to graph them. You learned how to assess the center and spread of datasets and how to identify relationships between variables using different types of graphs. Graphs often convey results more intuitively but can mislead.

Then, we moved on to summary statistics that use a single number to describe an entire dataset. These measures often complement graphs and answer the same types of questions. They include measures of central tendency, measures of variability, percentiles, and correlation.

Up next was probability distributions. Probability distributions help you understand the distribution of values, calculate probabilities, and are the foundation of hypothesis testing.

Collectively, this knowledge allows you to understand the basics of the different types of data, how to summarize a dataset, identify relationships between variables, and use probabilities to assess the distribution of values. These skills will allow you to summarize a dataset and convey its essence to others.

After covering the nitty-gritty details of working with data, we moved on to some broader concepts. We explored the differences between descriptive and inferential statistics. Both branches often use the same numeric summaries. However, there are additional requirements for being able to use a sample to learn about a population. For example, you'll need to use a random sampling technique and an analysis that accounts for random sampling error. You also learned about sample estimates versus population parameters, different sampling methodologies, random sampling error, and the importance of a large sample size.

Then, the book began to focus exclusively on scientific studies and how scientific studies require the use of inferential statistics. We looked at the scientific method and how to incorporate statistical analyses into a study. We progressed on to experimental designs and the importance of identifying causal relationships rather than just correlation. Different types of experiments face various challenges in ruling out alternative explanations. This portion of the book focuses on how science uses statistical methodologies to learn and expand the frontiers of human knowledge.

Finally, we finished the book by looking at different ways to critique scientific experiments, whether they're your own or another researcher's. We looked at criteria for establishing causality, the reliability and validity of the data, and the validity of the experiment.

To be able to draw sound scientific conclusions using an experiment, there is a long list of considerations, requirements, and methodologies that go well beyond just calculating the numbers.

Next Steps for Further Study

So, what's left to study? Plenty!

A logical place to continue is learning about hypothesis testing in more detail. This topic covers a variety of hypothesis tests, how they work, their assumptions, and proper interpretations. These procedures are essential, and we discussed them only briefly. They're the next step in using data to learn.

In this book, we covered how to set up contrasts in experimental designs and assess differences in outcomes. Hypothesis tests are the procedures that determine whether those differences, the effects, are statistically significant. Are the effects that you see in your sample data likely to exist in the population or can they be explained away as random sampling error?

In 2020, I published a book about hypothesis testing that explains how they work, how to use them correctly, and how to be sure you can trust the results. There are many different tests, and you must be sure that you're using the correct one for any given situation. It also includes confidence intervals, determining which probability distribution fits your data, and performing power analyses to estimate the correct sample size.

Regression analysis is another type of analysis that researchers use with inferential statistics and experimental designs. Regression creates statistical models that define the mathematical relationship between the independent and dependent variables. These models can contain many continuous and categorical variables and model different types of effects and curvature. Analysts can also use regression models to make predictions.

Researchers use regression for scientific studies, from true experiments with multiple factors to observational studies, when they need to understand the role of each variable and account for confounding variables. In this book, we looked at how an observational study about vitamin supplement consumption used regression analysis to control for a multitude of confounding variables.

Many of the other topics we've covered, you can learn about in much greater depth. For example, there are entire books written about various sampling methodologies to cover special needs and cases. Other books have been written about experimental designs, including those for very specialized uses.

My Other Books

Hypothesis Testing: An Intuitive Guide for Making Data Driven Decisions

Build a solid foundation for understanding how hypothesis tests work and become confident that you know when to use each type of test, how to use them properly to obtain reliable results, and interpret the results correctly. Chances are high that you'll need a working knowledge of hypothesis testing to produce new findings yourself and to understand the work of others. I present a wide variety of tests that assess characteristics of different data types. I focus on helping you grasp key concepts, methodologies, and procedures while deemphasizing equations. Learn how to use these tests painlessly!

In today's data-driven world, we hear about making decisions based on the data all the time. Hypothesis testing plays a crucial role in that process, whether you're in academia, making business decisions, or in quality improvement. Without hypothesis tests, you risk drawing the wrong conclusions and making bad decisions. The world today produces more data and more analyses designed to influence you than ever before. Are you ready for it?

In this 367-page book, build the skills and knowledge you'll need for effective hypothesis testing, including the following:

- Why you need hypothesis tests and how they work.
- Using significance levels, p-values, confidence intervals.
- Interpreting the results.
- Select the correct type of hypothesis test to answer your question.
- Learn how to test means, medians, variances, proportions, distributions, counts, correlations for continuous and categorical data, and outliers.

- One-Way ANOVA, Two-Way ANOVA and interaction effects.
- Estimate a good sample size for your study.
- Checking assumptions and obtaining reliable results.
- Manage the error rates for false positives and false negatives.
- Understand sampling distributions, central limit theorem, and statistical power.
- Know how t-tests, F-tests, chi-squared tests, and post hoc tests work.
- Learn about the differences between parametric, nonparametric, and bootstrapping methods.
- Examples of different types of hypothesis tests.
- Downloadable datasets so you can try it yourself.

Learn more about my Hypothesis Testing book on my website!

https://statisticsbyjim.com/store

Regression Analysis: An Intuitive Guide for Using and Interpreting Linear Models

Over the course of this full-length book, you'll progress from a beginner to a skilled practitioner. I'll help you intuitively understand regression analysis by focusing on concepts and graphs rather than equations and formulas. I use everyday language so you can grasp regression at a deeper level.

Learn practical tips for performing your analysis and interpreting the results. Feel confident that you're analyzing your data properly and able to trust your results. Know that you can detect and correct problems that arise.

This 336 page book covers the following:

- How regression works and when to use it.
- Selecting the correct type of regression analysis.
- Specifying the best model.
- Understanding main effects, interaction effects, and modeling curvature.
- Interpreting the results.
- Assessing the fit of the model.
- Generating predictions and evaluating their precision.
- Checking the assumptions and resolving issues.
- Downloadable datasets for the examples.
- Examples of different types of regression analyses.

Learn more about my Regression Analysis book on my website!

https://statisticsbyjim.com/store

References

You can find formulas and references for the procedures and methodology in basic statistics textbooks. I frequently use *Statistics* by Freedman et al. listed below. The other references apply to journal articles that I use as examples throughout this book.

Freedman, F. P. (1998). *Statistics (Third Edition).* New York: W.W. Norton & Company, Inc.

Hill, A. (1965). The Environment and Disease: Association or Causation? *Proceedings of the Royal Society of Medicine*, 295-300.

Monto, A., Ohmit, S., Petrie, J., Johnson, E., Truscon, R., Teich, E., . . . Victor, J. (2009). Comparative efficacy of inactivated and live attenuated influenza vaccines. *N Engl J Med.*, 1260-1267.

Mursu, J. R. (2011). Dietary Supplements and Mortality Rate in Older Women: The Iowa Women's Health Study. *Arch Intern Med.*, 1625-1633.

Recommended Citation for This Book

Frost, J. (2019). Introduction to statistics: An intuitive guide for analyzing data and unlocking discoveries. Statistics By Jim Publishing.

Index

About the Author

I'm Jim Frost, and I have extensive experience in academic research and consulting projects. In addition to my statistics website, I am a regular columnist for the American Society of Quality's *Statistics Digest*. Additionally, my most recent journal publication as a coauthor is *The Neutral Gas Properties of Extremely Isolated Early-Type Galaxies III* (2019) for the American Astronomical Society.

I've been the "data/stat guy" for research projects that range from osteoporosis prevention to analysis of online user behavior. My role has been to design the proper research settings, collect a large amount of valid measurements, and figure out what it all means. Typically, I'm the first person on the project to learn about new findings while interpreting the results of the statistical analysis. Even if the findings are not newsworthy, that thrill of discovery is an awesome job perk!

I love statistics and analyzing data! I've been performing statistical analysis on-the-job for 20 years and helping people learn statistics for over ten years at a statistical software company. I love talking and writing about statistics. While working at the statistical software company, I learned how to present statistics in a manner that makes statistics more intuitive.

I want to help you learn statistics. But I'm not talking about learning all the equations. Don't get me wrong. Equations are necessary. Equations are the framework that makes the magic, but the truly fascinating aspects are what it all means. I want you to learn the true essence of statistics. I'll help you intuitively understand statistics by focusing on concepts and graphs. After all, you use statistical software so you don't have to worry about the formulas and instead focus on understanding the results.

I've spent over a decade working at a major statistical software company. When you work on research projects, you generally use a regular group of statistical analyses. However, when you work at a statistical software company, you need to know of all the analyses that are in the software! I helped people use our software to gain insights and maximize the value of their own data regardless of their field.

Statistics is the field of learning from data. That's amazing. It gets to the very essence of discovery. Statistics facilitates the creation of new knowledge. Bit by bit, we push back the frontier of what is known. That is what I want to teach you! My goal is to help you to see statistics through my eyes–as a key that can unlock discoveries that are in your data.

The best thing about being a statistician is that you get to play in everyone's backyard. —John Tukey

I enthusiastically agree! If you have an inquisitive mind, statistical knowledge, and data, the potential is boundless. You can play in a broad range of intriguing backyards!

That interface between a muddled reality and obtaining orderly, valid data is an exciting place. This place ties together the lofty goals of scientists to the nitty-gritty nature of the real world. It's an interaction that I've written about extensively in this book and on my blog, and I plan to continue to do so. It's where the rubber meets the road.

One of the coolest things about the statistical analysis is that it provides you with a toolkit for exploring the unknown. Christopher Columbus needed many tools to navigate to the New World and make his discoveries. Statistics are the equivalent tools for the scientific explorer because they help you navigate the sea of data that you collect.

You'll be increasingly thankful for these tools when you see a worksheet filled with numbers and you're responsible for telling everyone what it all means.

Read more on my website: statisticsbyjim.com!

Made in the USA
Las Vegas, NV
29 January 2024